HOW DID YOU THINK OF THAT?

The *Chemistry in Action Series* has been designed to give the interested layman a thorough introduction to the many different sides of the chemical industry. Prepared under the joint supervision of the Education Activities Committee of the Manufacturing Chemists' Association and Doubleday & Company, Inc., each volume focuses on a particular segment of the chemical industry and relates the pure chemical science to the final products met in everyday life. The volumes have each been written by distinguished authorities in the field, and cover such various fields as agricultural chemistry, chemicals from the atmosphere and from the ocean, and the chemistry of paints, the soil, water purification, sulfuric acid, the silicon compounds, synthetic textiles, drugs, and antibiotics.

DAVID H. KILLEFFER is the author of over fifty books on industrial chemistry and hundreds of articles for both the professional and the layman. A chemical engineering graduate of the University of North Carolina, Mr. Killeffer was active in developing the field of public relations for the chemical industry, and, in 1957, he was awarded the first James T. Grady Medal of the American Chemical Society. In 1967, Mr. Killeffer was awarded the first Honor Scroll of the Florida Chapter of the American Institute of Chemists, which cited him "for his contributions to the profession of chemistry through his excellence as a scientist and a research administrator." Now retired after nearly fifty years in the chemical industry, Mr. Killeffer lives in Clearwater, Florida. His book CHEMICAL ENGINEERING is the first volume in the *Chemistry in Action Series.*

HOW DID YOU THINK OF THAT?

An Introduction to the Scientific Method

DAVID H. KILLEFFER

PREPARED UNDER THE SPONSORSHIP OF
THE MANUFACTURING CHEMISTS' ASSOCIATION

Garden City, New York

DOUBLEDAY & COMPANY, INC.

1969

Library of Congress Catalog Card Number 69–10974
Copyright © 1969 by David H. Killeffer
All Rights Reserved
Printed in the United States of America
First Edition

For Louis and John

Acknowledgment

Much of the material in this volume was treated from a somewhat different point of view in the author's previous book, *The Genius of Industrial Research,* and consequently many similarities exist between the two. Many volumes by others have been consulted in developing the theme. Some of these are quoted, and are listed in the bibliography that closes the volume. In addition to these sources, I have gathered information and points of view from many colleagues over several decades and feel deeply indebted to great numbers of friends among eminent (and not so eminent) scientists who have been helpful to me over the years. But I am especially indebted to Messrs. H. A. Braendle, Henry L. Cox, and William E. Beggs, who have read the manuscript and offered valuable suggestions; and to William E. Chace and W. C. Fernelius, who, heading up the *Chemistry in Action Series* for the Manufacturing Chemists' Association, have been guides, philosophers and friends in completing this part of the project. To all of these, my best thanks.

D.H.K.

CONTENTS

HOW DID YOU THINK OF THAT?

CHAPTER 1

You, Too, Can Use the Scientific Method

While Cinderella and her fairy godmother—in the Rodgers and Hammerstein operetta—are busy bewitching the pumpkin into a golden coach, they sing an "Impossible Song." The gist of it is that the world is full of impossible fools who do not believe in sensible rules, impossible dopes who build impossible hopes, but who make impossible things happen every day.

Those of us who no longer believe in the literal witchery of fairy godmothers might just possibly feel that these two joyous characters are singing about the modern scientific research worker. No one else wrecks so many traditionally "sensible rules"; no one else accomplishes so many "impossible things"; and certainly no one else builds so many "impossible hopes"—and fulfills them.

But Cinderellas and fairy godmothers, as all fairy-story characters must, skip airily over the hard fact that these "impossible things" require a vast amount of hard mental labor, a continual and purposeful flexing of the muscles of someone's mind, to give the waving of a fairy's wand its "impossible" magic. Behind all such modern magic lies a method of thinking out the answers to problems, of thinking up ways of overcoming all manner of difficulties and of getting us the things we want. Furthermore, each of us who expects to be successful in research must use that basic method, the scientific method. If we have no interest in research as a career, we can still profit by the same general method in meeting and solving our daily problems. If we are not scientists, we may prefer to call it "creative thinking"—another name for what scientists call research.

Let's look into it.

Millions of everyday problems, great and small, cease

to be problems when we apply creative thinking and imagination to them. No human activity seems to be so completely outside our control as this creative faculty. We commonly think of the creative process as sudden inspiration, a gift of God that comes to us in a sudden flash from outside ourselves and without our intervention. The enlightening flash of a new idea arriving, the long-sought solution to a problem, certainly seems beyond our ability to engender or prevent. Yet modern industry thrives through organized research that is simply the directed exercise of creative imagination.

Furthermore, if you happen not to have a fairy godmother handy to work magic for you, don't despair. Even if you are not a fullfledged genius yourself, you still can accomplish much, make your life far more fruitful, if you will use your inborn powers *methodically*.

The key lies in that last word—methodically. If we understand the pattern, the method, of creative thinking, and follow it thoughtfully, then we can turn the pumpkin of our thinking into our heart's desire. Perhaps your thinking, even though it may be as methodical as you please, may not yield a Rolls or a Cadillac or an Imperial, but at least it can materialize a vehicle that will get you where you want to go.

Don't let anyone tell you you can't think creatively; not even, and most especially, yourself. It just isn't so. Thinking, like everything else, is a matter of knowing how to use what natural ability we have, and then of practicing. For our brain, like our little finger, or our left hand, or our pitching arm, or our operatic voice, can shrivel and lose most of its useful ability if we don't give it practice. Maybe you can't be an Einstein or a Compton or a Galileo or a Copernicus. Very few of us, indeed, can. But at least you can be a better, more effective thinker than you are if you will use and practice the same method these men followed —the scientific method. Remember always that the ability to think creatively—the unique power of the human brain—

can also shrivel, and even vanish, when it is not exercised.

The trouble usually is that we fail to realize the powerful force for achievement, accomplishment, and happiness that the mere act of thinking may be. We thus never learn to use our talent and let it dry up and die from want of exercise.

With thinking, as with any other skill you might wish to learn, your best plan is to go to an expert to find out how it is done. Our most highly skilled and effective thinkers are our scientists, and you can learn from them. They, above all others, constantly exercise their thinking powers. And they seem to accomplish most by their thinking.

That sounds more awesome than it is. Creative thinking is not easy, but neither is it impossible, as we shall see by studying some typical cases.

Socrates, the ancient Greek philosopher, was the earliest creative thinker to leave us a record of his method. He recognized how lazy people are and how reluctant they are to think. He taught his disciples that creative thinking can only begin when and if the thinker senses and recognizes a problem, a stimulus, a "thorn in the mind," and then decides to do something about it. Clearly, where there is no problem, there is no incentive to think about it or to solve it. Only when a problem becomes irritating enough do we tackle its solution.

When some unknown genius became sufficiently irritated by the way his cheese or butter or hard-boiled egg stuck to the knife blade instead of coming away in neat slices, he created an edge without a blade. He realized that only the edge did the cutting and the rest of the knife blade served no useful function, but only stuck to his soft cheese to tear it. Then he went the next step and cut his cheese, or his butter, or his hard-boiled egg into neat slices by using a fine wire stretched taut, the edge of a bladeless knife. Simple as that sounds—and far removed from the glamorous intricacy of modern science—it was a creative act developing out of a creative analysis of a vexing situation—sloppy slices of soft, sticky stuffs. In that respect, our unnamed inventor employed thinking quite as creative as many of the feats of our best scientific minds.

So let us put down as the first necessity of creativity: a "thorn in the mind," a problem, an irregularity, that so irritates us that we are moved to do something about it.

Once we recognize that there exists a problem that irritates us to the point of trying to solve it, our next step is to state the problem in such terms that we can handle it. It is well enough to have the earning of a million dollars as our problem, but that may be both too ambitious and too indefinite for our particular abilities. Obviously, such an ambitious goal may simply baffle us and leave no reasonable problem for us to tackle. Only when it has been further broken down can we grasp it clearly enough to plan a way to achieve the desired result.

Perhaps the first breakdown would be to scratch that million-dollar goal and set up a more modest sum that we might be able to realize, and then to set about seeking ways to add that modest amount to our assets. If we go back to our stretched-wire cheese knife, then we might plan several ways that we could convert this idea into tangible assets: (a) using our new knife, we might slice cheese for other people for a fee; or (b) we might manufacture stretched-wire knives for sale; or (c) we might sell the design of our knife to someone else who might manufacture it for sale; or (d) we might apply for a patent on our idea and offer the patent for sale to a possible manufacturer. Any of these might set us on the way to acquire at least part of our million dollars. In any case, we have stated our problem in terms that could be solved by us. And that brings us to the second necessity of creativity: we must state our problem in such terms that we can solve it.

If we are to create, we must have raw material to form into our new concept. Sir Joshua Reynolds, the great English painter and a skillful creator, pointed out that creativity "consists in forming new combinations of images and ideas previously gathered and deposited in memory. Nothing can come of nothing; so if we have laid up no raw materials, we can produce no new combinations." Perhaps we should add that our accumulated materials must be stored in our minds in such order that they are available on call; that ideas and facts are neatly classified and not simply dumped in haphazard, disordered heaps that baffle our efforts to call them out when we need them.

There are many ways that we can increase our store of raw materials for the exercise of our creative faculties: (a) by drawing on our own experiences; (b) by tapping the accumulated experiences that others have stored in books and papers in our libraries; (c) by observing events that happen around us bearing upon the general field of our problem; (d) by seeking out situations that are like ours and have been solved; (e) by conducting experiments of a kind that will give us answers to some or all of the questions that arise in our minds about our major problem; and (f) by discussing all or parts of our major problem with others having experiences that will help us along our way. Each added bit of information bearing on our search may allow us to restate our problem in new terms that will be a little easier to handle.

Here comes the truly creative part: we must now choose suitable bits from our store of raw material and assemble them in such new combinations that they solve our problem. Perhaps we know of another similar problem and can use that as a pattern for our solution. Or perhaps we must try a great many combinations of our bits of raw material before we find one that suits our purpose. Perhaps, too, we may reach some partial solution that sends us off searching for a missing piece or pieces to complete our pattern. The process is somewhat like assembling a jigsaw puzzle, but with one important difference: you know that you have all the pieces needed to form the jigsaw picture, but when you are thinking in some quite new direction, you can never be sure at any moment that you have everything you need.

Finally, you must cap the whole enterprise by trying your solution to be sure that it is the solution you want. Here you learn whether your bladeless knife will really cut cheese into neat slices, or whether something else is needed, some modification of the taut-wire solution, to make it work. At this stage, too, it may be necessary to go back to the very beginning and start over again.

Thus we have subdivided our creative thinking, our research method, at the outset into five steps that lead us toward our answer:

(1) Consciousness of a problem;
(2) Stating the problem;
(3) Assembling the elements of a solution;
(4) Choosing from these and combining them into a solution; and finally
(5) Subjecting our solution to trial to prove whether or not it is a valid solution.

There are a number of other ways to set up these several steps of creative thinking and problem solving, some of which we shall note later. Perhaps the series one of my close friends employs may appeal to you:

(1) Recognition;
(2) Definition;
(3) Preparation;
(4) Incubation;
(5) Inspiration;
(6) Confirmation; and
(7) Remuneration.

Or you may prefer the series headings (preparation, incubation, illumination, and verification) proposed by Graham Wallas, which we shall discuss later. The statement of the several steps may vary considerably, depending on one's particular point of view. But, in the long run, the subject matter covered is the same; its subdivisions have merely been arrived at by expressing different points of view. Perhaps the addition of remuneration to our list is significant. It emphasizes the commercial aspect of research, but of course remuneration can as easily take the form of personal satisfaction in an accomplishment as it might the pecuniary rewards offered by industry. However these steps are stated or subdivided, the overall picture is the same: a methodical progression from a problem to a solution, from a "thorn in the mind" to a useful and usable solution. There we have the "thinking" part of our research, the vital core of the scientific method.

At the very beginning, or at any stage in our search, we may be able to form an hypothesis, or a theory, about our problem and its solution that can become a road map to guide our way ahead. Obviously, what we learn as we proceed may very well change our ideas about our problem and require us to revise or replace the road map that served well before.

This step-by-step confirmation or revision of our thinking about our problem is the basis of the scientific method. It recognizes varying degrees of accuracy and of confirmation of our ideas, and it revises and progressively narrows our hypothesis, or theory, to increase its value. If we ignore or neglect these basic concepts of the scientific method, then the methods of research become inscrutable. In the light of them, we can see significant patterns in the solution of problems, great and small.

When we study the accomplishments of great minds, we find that they accomplish their miracles sometimes by what seems to themselves a kind of inspired magic, but far more often by a methodical following of some such pattern as we have outlined. Often, an individual deeply saturated with his subject (having a well-stocked mental storehouse of raw materials for his thinking) may seem to progress from problem to solution by giant steps, without following the whole pattern in detail. There are such geniuses, of course, but most of the necessary work of the world must be done by persons who consciously develop whatever skill they have instead of receiving it at birth. Let's follow through with that idea and see if we cannot develop for ourselves methods that will help us to become more useful in our particular worlds.

CHAPTER 2

What Is Our Problem?

Graham Wallas, the British philosopher, tells us: "Our mind is not likely to give us a clear answer to any particular problem unless we set it a clear question, and we are more likely to notice the significance of any new piece of evidence, or new association of ideas, if we have formed a definite conception of a case to be proved or disproved."

The most important step in any creative thinking or research is to *understand* the problem. Understanding is essential to stating it clearly and correctly. The significance of the terms in which we state a problem may be clearer if we discuss an example. Because it is a common problem (almost universal in industry), let's think about the scaling caused by hard water in a boiler. Almost every industry has some sort of problem with its steam-boiler water, and many a housewife is bothered by scale in her teakettle.

Control of the crystallization of calcium sulfate from boiler water to prevent the forming of scale that attaches itself firmly to the boiler may be stated in almost any number of ways; the terms depend upon who is making the statement and what the statement's purpose is. The stockholders would think of boiler scale only if it became a question of dividends. The directors might think of it as affecting efficiency of operation. To the president, it would be a matter of the diligence of the works manager, and the works manager would look to the superintendent, who in turn would question the plant engineer. Finally, at long last, the director of research might be given the problem, but most probably in the form of a question of the efficiency of the power plant. The hostess might simply worry about the flavor of her tea or the cleanliness of her kettle.

At this point industry finds a great many solutions possible: the company might purchase power instead of producing its own; it might seek a new source of boiler water; it might exchange steam turbines for diesel engines; it might install a water-treating plant; it might change the blow-down cycle of the boilers to throw out much of the scale as it is formed; and, finally, it might initiate a search for a method of flocculating calcium sulfate to prevent it from forming hard adherent scale inside the boiler.

Only when the problem is stated in some such terms as these last is it a proper subject to turn over to an individual in the research department as soluble by the methods of research. It must already have undergone a succession of narrowing operations to bring both problem and solution into focus.

An ability to accept problems in the most general terms and then to restate, analyze, and subdivide them is a skill of highest value in any problem-solving process. Possession of this skill is a necessity for efficient research. Without it, there can be no solution. Research may supply information to management to help decide between purchased and produced power, between steam and diesel, and between other like alternatives, but these are primarily problems of management and not of research. Not only must it be possible to break problems down into parts that can be handled, but management must understand what research is about and how it fits into the overall plan of the company.

An example is our problem of preventing the scale in a boiler. If the researcher thinks of such problems as indefinite and has no idea of how to determine beforehand the physical or chemical characteristics of a compound that will suppress scaling, the search seems hopeless. Perhaps any one of a thousand different chemical compounds would serve. Lacking any theory, the only recourse is to the "shotgun" Edisonian method of trying everything and hoping for a lead. This would require developing a test, stocking the laboratory with these thousand compounds, and then putting one after another through the test. The search becomes even more hopeless when we realize that concentration may be important, and may require us to test each individual compound at a great many different concentrations. This could require several years' work and might lead nowhere.

Preliminary experiments would suggest that this problem could be solved by controlling the crystal growth of the scale, and that substances most strongly affecting growth of crystals from a water solution also tend to concentrate at the metal-liquid interface. Furthermore, substances tending to concentrate at this interface are known to decrease the surface tension of the solution. This provides a working theory. The original thousand possible compounds are narrowed by reasoning alone to one class: surface-tension depressors. For the initial test we should select something used before for a similar purpose, namely, tannic acid. Early experiments would show that this compound has a distinct, favorable effect, but that the basic conditions of the problem do not require a structure as complicated as tannic acid, which seems to be unstable. Apparently, tannic acid undergoes hydrolysis, yielding gallic acid as one of the reaction products. This simpler compound of relatively simple structure, but which still meets the basic requirements, proves best of all in further tests.

Thus a positive result is reached in a short time by first devising a theory based on experience or the literature. The investigation can continue along the same lines and perhaps uncover a reagent which will prevent the formation not only of calcium sulfate scale but of other scales as well. The researcher's ideas have now "risen to the dignity of an invention," and he may be amply rewarded for his pains and trouble.

In any event, the researcher has learned something valuable about this type of problem. He has not been forced to lie awake nights or to cudgel his brain trying to conjure into being a marvelous inspiration that will overcome his difficulties. Furthermore, the manual labor has been relatively small, something that is bound to please any researcher, amateur or professional.

Neither tannic nor gallic acid is quite suitable to use in the household teakettle, either to prevent or remove scale. But our investigation so far *has* shown how easiest to clean up the family teakettle. Every modern household has one, if not several, synthetic detergents ready at hand and, since these compounds depend for their value on depressing surface tension, they immediately suggest themselves as fitting the criterion for scale prevention we have reached. Hot water has a lower surface tension than cold, so the ideal conditions for trying out our idea in the teakettle are a little detergent (a low-sudsing one by preference) dissolved in hot water, and that allowed to stand in the kettle. If that does not loosen the scale, then a couple of spoonfuls or so of vinegar (the most readily available household acid) added to the detergent solution may very well loosen the scale so that it is easily removed and rinsed out.

Lack of understanding by management of the nature of research sometimes leads to weird results. A company president once posed the following problem to me to suggest the value of co-operating with him. Said he: "I have an idea for a paint remover that will avoid all present patents and make them useless. The mixtures we use now simply soften the paint; you still have to remove it afterward. My new remover would actually take the paint off the wall so that it could be swept up from the floor." "Well," said I, "that is wonderful and should make your fortune. What do you want me to do about it?" "Oh," said my friend, "I want you to tell me what to put in it!"

Even though that problem was all solved a half century ago, except for the essential detail of what to put in the product to make it function in that way, nothing of the kind has yet appeared on the market. Attempts to state the problem of such a composition in a form that can be solved suggest the reasons for this. Such a composition might use either of two kinds of softening agents already widely used in paint and varnish removers: an alkali to convert the paint film into water-soluble form; or an organic solvent that would dissolve, swell, or soften the film to be removed.

The use of alkalies to dissolve paint films is well known. Metal parts can be completely cleaned by dipping them in a caustic lye of an appropriate concentration and temperature. There is even an effective alkali remover for application to large objects (too large to immerse), which consists of a strong caustic lye to which a starch has been added for the purpose of holding the lye in a moist, active condition against the paint surface. If lye alone is spread on a surface, the solution drains off or its water content quickly evaporates and leaves the caustic dry and unreactive in contact with the incompletely attacked paint film. Adding starch to the lye before applying it to the paint film changes both its adhesion to the surface and its moisture-holding characteristic; and the starch-lye holds the caustic in a moist layer on the surface to be cleaned. Because the starch swells in the lye, the paste also shrinks greatly as it dries. Thus, if a caustic-starch paste is applied to a surface and allowed to dry, the resulting layer will pull up into concave chips through the greater contraction of the outer surface because of its more rapid drying.

That would seem to indicate one direction for investigation, but unfortunately the caustic-starch paste remover has several apparently insuperable drawbacks to its general application. Most important of these is the attack of the caustic on wood and the difficulty of removing all the caustic from the wood surface after the oil-paint film has been softened and removed. Caustic roughens the surface of wood, a serious fault expensive to correct if the surface is to be refinished, and any slight residue of alkali in or on the surface would injure the new finish applied over it. Washing woodwork with water, necessary to remove caustic, may also injure its surface.

When a caustic-starch paste remover is applied to metal

surfaces, for which it is admirably suited, the paste and the old paint film, now practically saponified, can be easily, quickly, and completely flushed off with water without injury to the metal surface. The surface needs only to dry to be in a condition ideal for refinishing.

Another interesting possibility would be to produce some such effect with a paste based on organic solvents instead of water, thereby utilizing the solvent effects of organic compounds instead of the saponifying action of lye. The present well-known paint and varnish removers are formulated to include, first, mixed solvents capable of softening and/or dissolving the paint film and, second, a nonvolatile constituent to retard the evaporation of the solvent mixture.

Nitrocellulose and vulcanized rubber, for instance, have the property of swelling in certain organic solvents, much as starch does in alkali, and might thus be employed under some yet unknown conditions to produce an effect of the kind desired.

The drawback, of course, is that the curling action of unequal drying of either type of material requires that the curling film approach dryness, whereas the softening of the paint film requires the moist condition produced by a relatively high concentration of solvent. Furthermore, the adhesion between the softened paint film that is to be pulled off and the drying layer of paste may be considerably less than the adhesion of the paint film to the surface, even when substantially dissolved by the remover. Preliminary experiments along these lines quickly proved too discouraging to justify further pursuit of the idea.

Obviously, such a paint remover must perform a service of enough added value to pay for the added cost of the improved product and for the research, development, and sales expense required to put it in the users' hands. That requires a knowledge of the possible users, the purposes for which they might employ the product, and the value it might be to them in competition with other materials and methods for reaching the same results. In the case in point, even a cursory examination reveals the possibilities of profit to be too small to justify an extensive research.

Actually, that problem belongs in the same pigeonhole with one seriously proposed to the late Allen Rogers during the extreme shortage of fast dyes during World War I. A visitor one afternoon sought the professor's help on what he said was an important problem. It had to do, he said, with a fast black dye that would resist any amount of any kind of mistreatment without fading. Dr. Rogers was immediately interested and asked for details. The visitor then insisted that every precaution be taken against eavesdroppers, and only when he was fully assured on this point and convinced of the trustworthiness of the professor did he reveal his idea. "Carbon," said he, "is absolutely permanently black and it blacks everything it touches. It should be able to impart this permanent blackness to a fabric immersed in a solution of carbon. What I want you to tell me, Dr. Rogers, is some good cheap solvent for carbon that will serve that purpose!"

It is hardly necessary to point out that the only known solvent for carbon is molten iron and that molten iron is hardly the kind of stuff one would choose for a dye bath to dye milady's silks.

There is, of course, the possibility of creating a bond (like that presumed to exist in rubber compounds) between the excessively fine colloidal particles of carbon black and the molecules comprising the filaments of textile fabrics. One might thus approach the ideal permanent black dye by establishing a colloidal or a chemical bond between carbon particles of almost-molecular dimensions and the huge molecules of textile fibers. This might be direct or through some intermediate stuff. Interesting speculation! But also a highly practical solution of the problem of a permanent black in synthetic fibers!

Great numbers of unsolved research problems remain unsolved because they have not been properly stated. Before they can be solved it is most often necessary to state them clearly and to subdivide them into bits that can be solved. By thus "nibbling" away at a big problem—our desire for a million dollars, for instance—we can ultimately reduce it to a size we can handle.

In a different manner, new facts discovered or new investigative methods may help the nibbling. We can hopefully re-examine our bafflers whenever an important scientific advance or a new method opens new possibilities of success. The electron microscope, for instance, provided an eye far more deeply penetrating than had ever before been available to microscopists and thus justified a re-examination of problems involving colloidal and amorphous particles. A number of puzzling questions about pigments were at once solved by electron examinations. The development of pH measuring techniques (specifying degrees of acidity or alkalinity) answered great numbers of problems that had previously been insoluble. Problems of tanning, fermentation, and other processes involving proteins have been solved through control of pH.

Often, the statement of a problem requires new facts revealed by some new instrument or technique to make it soluble. T. F. Bradley's research at American Cyanamid Company on the alkali isomerization of drying oils is a case in point. The problem was to increase the unsaturation of fatty oils, or the conjugation of their double bonds, to allow plentiful non-drying and semi-drying oils to replace drying oils unobtainable because of World War II.

Two types of structure characterize the best drying oils and seem closely coupled with the drying property: double bonds (unsaturation) and conjugation of double bonds (that is, pairs of double bonds connected to neighboring carbon atoms). While unsaturation is essential to drying, conjugation enormously enhances the drying property of each unit of unsaturation. Now, while unsaturation is as readily and accurately determined as the iodine number, chemical determination of degree of conjugation is not simple, nor do the results have any considerable degree of precision. In fact, analyses for degree of conjugation by chemical methods are little more than guided guesses and may lead nowhere.

Now, the method of isomerization under investigation by Bradley consisted of heating the fatty acid with an excess of alkali. Theory indicated that this reaction would succeed, but the change in conjugation effected by this treatment was less than the limit of error of the method. Under the circumstances, no trends showed up in a long series of tests.

The whole line of investigation was about to be abandoned when the far more accurate and penetrating ultraviolet spectroscopic method of determining conjugation was tried. Immediately, a trend became apparent from the reanalyses of samples already prepared and that indicated the direction subsequent experiments should take. Following the new direction led to prompt success.

The basic pattern of industrial research applies equally well to individuals or to groups that are engaged not necessarily in solving the great problems of our day and age, but merely in working out the problems of daily living. If a group can be gathered together to focus upon a single problem, the results usually are considerably better than the sum of the accomplishments of the same individuals working singly. This is a rather striking example of synergy, the working together of several minds or individuals.

The efficiency of the whole operation depends upon a systematic attack on the problem. And in order to make any progress at all the problem must be clearly stated. Moreover, it must be stated in terms that can be solved. Indeed, the whole process of industrial research centers around progressive restatements of the problem as bits are "nibbled off" of the great problem by successive solutions of smaller, corollary problems.

Perhaps the best way to make clear just what this means

will be to look at another example. Recently, a young man came to see me in some distress. He had become thoroughly unhappy in his job, but because he had a wife and child he could not afford to quit and then look for something he might like. He had been to psychological counselors and had been told that his aptitudes fitted his present line of work and that he should stay at it. He had been employed (and still was) in the advertising department of a daily newspaper somewhat above average size. He could not afford to make another connection that would not be a good one, nor could he risk being out of work for any period of time. So it was necessary to hold his present job and look for another as effectively as possible. The method (or lack of it) he had followed was to try here and there without setting up a pattern for himself, and indeed without deciding in his own mind just what he wanted to do. That spread his efforts too thin and left him without results to show for his efforts. The obvious application of the scientific method to his problem very soon enabled him to pinpoint his efforts on a few possible answers and thus to get results quickly. The first selection was based on his desire to work for a selling organization of a producer, rather than for a publication or a selling group. That immediately brought his possibilities down to about 10 per cent of the total possibles. Next, he wanted to work for a company producing consumer goods (as distinct from producers' goods not sold directly to the public). That narrowed the field still further and when he set up the size of the company he thought would suit him, he had reduced the possibles in the territory he preferred to a small enough number so that he could study each individually and concentrate on a single one with the others as "spares."

This simple illustration demonstrates the power of the scientific method as applied to an everyday problem. Furthermore, it shows the extremely effective way that progressive restatement of the problem (in this case, limiting the scope of the man's search for a job) leads rapidly closer to the desired solution. Put in other terms, the scientific method seeks answers by narrowing the field of inquiry and by restating the problem in a variety of ways by a successive series of statements that can be answered by yes or no. Finally, the area in which the answer may be found is shrunk so far that it can all be investigated; or the answer itself becomes self-evident.

The efficiency of any investigation is highest when the problem can be specifically and simply stated. The more specific the problem, the greater the efficiency of solving it. An indefinite or ill-defined problem can only elicit an indefinite and ill-defined answer. Such lack of definition requires that the principal problem be subdivided into simpler ones that can be individually solved until the area left to investigate is easily covered.

As in the case of the puzzled job-hunter sketched above, the most effective way is to divide possibilities into probable and improbable on as many successive bases as may be applicable. No better device exists to save time and energy than to narrow the possibilities as far as possible as early as possible, preferably at the outset. Once the shrinking process has been carried as far as possible by either the selection of probables vs. improbables or the nibbling off and exclusion of obviously unfruitful areas around the periphery of the principal problem, then the remaining area can be investigated thoroughly.

Usually the problem bears some resemblance to other familiar ones, or we can develop analogies from previous experiences that will help define what we are looking for in terms we can use. Our illustrations of the boiler scale and the young man at a loss in his job are cases in point.

But occasionally the problem and its solution lie in totally new areas where no specific experience can guide us. The classic example is Edison's search for a carbon filament for his incandescent electric lamp. He wanted to produce in his filament the highest possible temperature and that led him to think of carbon, because of its extremely high melting point. But up to that time no one had succeeded in making a wire of carbon. So Edison experimented with every kind of fiber that he could lay his hands on, hoping by carbonizing the cellulose of the fiber that he would produce a fine filament of carbon. After many thousands of experiments, he found bamboo to be best for his purpose, and for many years electric lights employed filaments of carbonized bamboo. Even though the light was not very bright and the life of the filament was short, this was a key advance in the art of lighting.

Edison followed the method of Sir Francis Bacon in thus carrying out enormous numbers of experiments designed to clarify his problem and to enable him to state it in a solvable form. Usually this is the method used in entirely new, unexplored areas. John V. N. Dorr, who as a young man worked with Edison and later became eminent himself (as we shall see in another place), said that Edison, as a self-educated man with little formal schooling, distrusted books and far preferred to rely on his own observations, rather than on what he considered the untrustworthy writings of others. Thus he shut himself off from any but his own experience and built that up by untiring experimentation.

Once you are able to state your problem so that it may be reasonably solved, either in whole or by parts, you are well on your way. The heartbreak comes only when you find that you have not recognized your real problem but have wasted your effort in the futile search for the wrong objectives! We shall later have something to say about misleading theories constructed on faulty observation or unsound thinking, but before that it will be well to think about scientific methods that have succeeded.

CHAPTER 3

Two Approaches to a Solution

Basic to the scientific method is the fundamental axiom that our physical universe is a rational, ordered one in which cause and effect are inevitably linked and where events fit together in logical patterns. This concept is essential to all our thinking and to all our efforts to extend our knowledge. On the face of it, it is obviously true and must be so, since, otherwise, all of our highly successful efforts through research, investigation, and creative thinking to extend our knowledge usefully would have ended in futility. It is an axiom since it is a self-evident truth that cannot be directly proved by any means that we know. At that, we must not forget that this, like many other ideas once considered axiomatic, may at some future time be disproved by some yet undiscovered fact revealed by a yet undevised method of reasoning.

There, in what may be too small a nutshell, is the meat of the scientific method that has proved to be so eminently useful in the development of our lives: a tightly inter-woven fabric of facts that have been questioned and proved true and that form a part of a rational pattern. From such a basic pattern, once discovered and proved, the creative mind can reach out into hitherto unexplored regions and add to the pattern in new areas and directions. The method itself is valid, whatever may be our particular problem, whether we are faced with problems of inter-stellar travel or if ours is the simpler one of deciding whether to buy our family detergent in the package labeled apartment size or to splurge on the giant economy size. The method of thinking is basically the same, even though the problems may be vastly different in every other respect, and even though circumstances may require that we modify our fundamental pattern from time to time in some of its details.

Perhaps the most important circumstances influencing the detailed method are the objectives of our search. On the one hand, what is called academic, or pure, research concerns itself with a search for truth, for answers to questions, that need have no other motive and no compelling urgency beyond the satisfaction of solving the problem. That is a little like the urge that a man may feel to climb mountains "just because they are there," and not for any other objective than the satisfaction of overcoming difficulties. If, on the way up or down from the summit, some useful methods of climbing or descending are discovered or if some useful plant or mineral is found, that is a kind of extra value, a lagniappe, as they say in New Orleans. Or perhaps our academic research might be like a Sunday afternoon stroll that might wander through a beautiful park or an interesting old part of town on the way to the post office. On a stroll like that, one would take his time and stop to look more closely at a tree, a flower, a soccer game, that might contribute to the enjoyment of the journey. He would enjoy the walk for its own sake, and if the letter was mailed, that would be an added value.

In a certain contrast to this is what is commonly classed as industrial research. This is characterized by its more or less direct course toward a specific objective, the solution of some more or less definite problem having important implications, usually economic. It is as if our mountain climber set out to test some equipment for living in the rarefied cold near the summit, or he might have determined to find out just what valuable minerals might be imbedded in the rocks at high altitudes. Our Sunday afternoon stroll would take on a much less leisurely character and, in the frame of industrial research, we would choose the most direct route to the post office to mail our letter, and let only the most important considerations lead us into the kinds of detours that make the academic approach so pleasant.

Usually, an academic research is carried on by an individual or a small team, since at the beginning there is seldom either the pressure to complete the search quickly or the finances to pay for speed. If subsequent developments change these circumstances, one can then adapt to them. In contrast, the industrial problem may very well offer such an economic reward for its solution that a team of workers may be under constant pressure to find the right answer.

Obviously, the differences, if any, between academic (pure) research and its industrial counterpart grow directly out of these fundamental differences in their objectives, their reasonably expected rewards, and the pressure and support (or lack of either) that may be inherent in them. The thinking and the experimental activities of both academic and industrial research workers follow the same patterns and so it is not important to this discussion to dwell further on these differences. Much more important to the whole picture of our scientific method are the approaches to problem solving that successful research workers in both categories have developed and used. Furthermore, only the tools of the scientific research worker differentiate his original creative thinking from that of poets, painters, authors, dramatists, and all the thousand and one other creative thinkers.

Research is primarily a mental activity—creative thinking—using physical processes of investigation. One must observe accurately and it is utterly essential to reason carefully from observations. Without both observation and deduction, research fails. A number of eminent scientists have from time to time emphasized one or the other of these two phases of research, but no successful worker has ever become so without employing both. It is, of course, true that several researchers may approach an utterly new problem quite differently, emphasizing either theory or experiment. One approach will succeed about as often as the other, and either alone is equally likely to be misleading under other circumstances.

Already in our discussion of the statement of the problem, we have touched briefly on the two principal approaches to research, the Baconian-Edisonian method of great numbers of experiments or observations from which one draws conclusions and a theory; and the Aristotle-Bancroft approach, based on forming a theory first and then seeking to prove or disprove it by experiment. Both of these approaches are highly successful, and the rare thing is to find any research that does not employ both approaches alternately or some compromise between them. Some research workers are able to assemble a very few experiments or observations into a tentative theory that then may need only to be tested to give the answer sought for. This is the method of the Greek philosopher Aristotle, who depended upon pure reason uninfluenced by specific experiments and whose teachings on research were strongly advocated in our modern world by the late Wilder D. Bancroft of Cornell University. Others (and that includes most of us) need greater numbers of facts before they can draw useful conclusions.

Thomas A. Edison, "the wizard of Menlo Park," was an eminent proponent of the Baconian "try-it-and-see" school of research, and the method emphasizing experiment has come to be better known today by his name than by that of Sir Francis Bacon, eminent in Elizabethan England. The Edisonian method consists in trying everything, watching the results closely, and hoping for light. As observations are piled upon each other, their very mass is expected to lead to the right answer. Actually, many answers often clamor for recognition. To find the right one becomes somewhat like seeking a needle in a haystack; every straw must be inspected to see whether the needle is in it.

Frequently, this is the only method available when entering upon an entirely new field, as George Oenslager did in rubber vulcanization, as we shall see later, and as Edison did in undertaking to find a filament for his incandescent lamp. The story of Edison's search for a material from which to produce a carbon filament able to withstand the hazards of lamp operation is well known. The search penetrated into most parts of the world and into the animal, vegetable, and mineral kingdoms. The only thread of theory extending through the whole was the permanence of carbon at high temperature. The final result, a reasonably good carbon filament, was far short of the present tungsten filament; but then, the subsequent research leading through tantalum to tungsten was undertaken only after the pioneer search for the carbon filament had succeeded!

While we ordinarily forget that the Greek Hippocrates, the father of medicine, was an important research worker, it is undeniable that his great value to humanity lay in researches into the nature of disease, upon which treatment of patients was later systematized. He was reaching out for general theories to connect and give meaning to the immense numbers of observations of patients and symptoms which had to serve as experiments in that early day of medicine. Hippocrates analyzed the phenomena of disease into elements and built a theory on his observations. Throughout a great part of his work, Hippocrates moved step by step toward the widest generalizations. He sought a natural history of acute disease (or, at least, of those acute diseases prevalent among his patients). His success was great, and the whole history of science goes far to support the view that such a methodical procedure is necessary in the development of a science that deals with complex and various phenomena. Here we have an ancient Greek practicing a method now known by the names of two very much later investigators, Bacon and Edison.

The opposite method, based on theory, was championed

in recent years by the late Wilder D. Bancroft, eminent physical chemist and founder and long-time editor of the *Journal of Physical Chemistry*. Whereas Edison amassed great numbers of facts, finally reaching a theory to help the search along, Bancroft's method begins with the formulation of a theory and continues with a search for facts to confirm it. Bancroft repeatedly asserted the sanctity of theory, even in the face of experimental contradiction and constantly insisted on a re-examination of experiments and observations that failed to fit in with the preconceived theory. Only under the strongest compulsion, he maintained, should a researcher abandon a well conceived and carefully thought out theory, and then only for another one. Without a theory to connect them, he has said, facts might as well not exist, since they have no individual meanings. That was also the view of Aristotle, who scarcely recognized experiments at all.

Obviously these two theories of research are both useful. At times, one approach will succeed, and at others it will as surely fail. The reasonable approach to solving any problem in the overwhelming majority of cases combines both methods. When the whole matter is entirely new and one has no clues, it is only reasonable to try everything that suggests itself, observing results with minute care. As results accumulate, a pattern may be discernible and a theory can then be formulated.

The method of pure experiment recognizes no experience or previously accumulated data. In the extreme case, one ignores preconceived notions and ideas. That is manifestly impossible, since no one can keep his mind blank for long on any subject of his active thinking. Vast numbers of experiments or observations are necessary in exploring hitherto unknown or unexplored fields or subjects. We shall note how this method was used by Oenslager in arriving at the important family of vulcanization accelerators for rubber. Several decades before, Darwin had reached his theory of evolution from consideration and digestion of thousands upon thousands of observations. Actually, Darwin's active accumulation of observations extended over a period of some twenty years.

On the other hand, the advocate of theory unshakable by experiment takes the contrasting view: that only one's experience can properly lead to a true solution of any problem. That is quite as false as the opposite view; but both have much to commend them when tempered with common sense and judgment. More reasonably stated, Bancroft placed greater reliance on experiences that have undergone a process of mental digestion than upon new observations—a distinction between seasoned judgment and snap decisions. Bancroft repeatedly cautioned against allowing ourselves to be swayed by small numbers of experiments that violate a logical rule, and against misleading experiments pointing to conclusions at violent odds with experience and judgment.

Oenslager, working at Diamond Rubber Company, used an experimental method similar to Edison's in his researches into the vulcanization of rubber. His original problem was to use cheaper gums related to rubber in producing pneumatic automobile tires, which in his day (before 1907) were already in mounting demand. To understand just what Oenslager did, we must picture the rubber tire industry as it was then, a very different operation from today's.

A typical rubber formula of that day might include 100 parts of fine Pará rubber, 62.5 parts of zinc oxide, and 6.25 parts of sulfur. When this dough was vulcanized for 90 minutes at 287°F., it would develop a tensile strength (resistance to being pulled apart) of 2,800 pounds per square inch. When a lower grade rubber (Corinto) was substituted for fine Pará, the curing required half an hour longer and the product had only half (or less) the tensile strength. So Oenslager's overall problem was to find a way to upgrade the product made from cheap rubber and shorten the time of cure. The reward for success in his research was tremendous in terms of 1905 thinking. If he could produce high quality rubber articles from cheap, low quality Pontianac rubber, for instance, he might effect a saving of a dollar a pound of rubber, and that comes to $20,000 per day on a ten-ton production.

Oenslager had very little to guide him. At the time he was working, the idea of catalysts, promoters of chemical reactions, was prominent in chemical thinking. So he sought a catalyst for the vulcanization reaction by trying out additions of small amounts of every kind of compound available to him, and some others he had to search out. The details are not important to us now, but his search finally revealed that mercuric iodide added to the dough we have mentioned above shortened the time of cure at the same temperature from two hours to twenty minutes and simultaneously raised the tensile strength of the product from 1,200 to 2,600 pounds per square inch. No basis for selecting a mercury compound could be found in his own experiences or those of others, and its useful properties could only be discovered by trying out a great many compounds, including mercury salts, and observing their effects. You might say that Oenslager "stumbled" upon this result, but, as Charles F. Kettering put it, "you can't stumble while you are sitting still"; furthermore, you must be able to recognize a useful "stumble" and know what it was you stumbled upon.

When tires were built with the new formula rubber and subjected to road tests, they failed miserably, but at least they demonstrated that the vulcanization reaction could be catalyzed by at least one substance. If one, why not others that might very well be better than the first one found? From this point, Oenslager backtracked on his reasoning and concluded that it might be useful to examine a variety of organic bases, since the lime, litharge, and magnesia that had been used in rubber doughs were all basic (this was before the concept of pH had been fully developed). When he tried aniline, then the cheapest organic base available to him, it worked! Subsequently, a product of the reaction of aniline with carbon disulfide, thiocarbanilide, proved even better than aniline and was without its objectionable toxic properties. Not only does this catalyst permit the use of low-grade rubbers in high-grade products, but it also improves the performance of high-grade rubbers. For example, adding 3 per cent thiocarbanilide to the then standard tire-tread batch gave a product having a tensile strength of 2,500 pounds per square inch after 60 minutes at 287°F. Now, if the dose of accelerator is doubled, the cure is effected in ten minutes and the tensile strength then is 3,000 pounds per square inch. Not only is the tensile strength of the rubber raised, but at the same time the shorter cure substantially raises the possible output of each vulcanizer, both important economies.

Oenslager's original work, for which he received the Perkin Medal in 1933, showed many others that improvements could be effected in tires by additions to the rubber, and the results are obvious to all today in our tremendously better tires. But the whole thing has hinged on Oenslager's wide-ranging exploratory experiments, which enabled him ultimately to state his problem in terms he could solve.

Nobel laureate Irving Langmuir's researches at the General Electric Company into high vacua ultimately led to enormous improvement in incandescent electric lights and effected huge savings in the cost of lighting that continue to pay dividends in better seeing.

Langmuir's work in the development of the gas-filled incandescent electric lamp grew out of an excursion around the General Electric laboratory in order to find some suitable subject for study during a summer vacation from his teaching duties at Stevens Institute.

The laboratory was engaged in developing drawn tungsten wire by the then new Coolidge process. A serious difficulty was the "offsetting" of the filaments, a kind of brittleness which appeared only when the lamps were run on alternating current. Out of a large number of samples of wire, three samples gave lamps that ran as well with alternating current as with direct current; no one knew why. Langmuir thought that one factor that had not been considered was that the offsetting might possibly be caused by gaseous impurities in the wire. He suggested heating various samples of wire in high vacuum and measuring the quantities of gas evolved.

The filaments, he found, gave off surprisingly large quantities of gas. Something entirely strange must be going on, because in a couple of days a small filament yielded a quantity of gas at atmospheric pressure that measured 7,000 times the volume of the filament, and even then there was no indication that gas evolution was going to stop. Langmuir spent most of the summer trying to find where this gas came from, and never did investigate the different samples of wire to see how much gas they contained.

He did learn that glass surfaces which have not been heated a long time in vacuum slowly give off water vapor, and this reacts with a tungsten filament to produce hydrogen, and also that the vapors of vaseline from a ground-glass joint in the vacuum system give off hydrocarbon vapors, which produce hydrogen and carbon monoxide.

Langmuir continued experiments on the sources of gas within vacuum apparatus, and studied the effects of introducing various gases into tungsten filament lamps. No two gases acted alike. Oxygen attacked the filament and formed tungstic oxide, WO_3. That seemed simple enough, but the kinetics of the reaction were not so simple.

A limited amount of hydrogen disappeared, apparently absorbed on the bulb in a chemically active form capable of reacting with oxygen at room temperature, even after the tungsten filament had been allowed to cool. This suggested hydrogen in atomic form. A large number of experiments, extending over several years, were made in a study of atomic hydrogen. Nearly all of these experiments would have seemed quite useless, or even foolish, as part of a direct and logical attack on the problem of improving tungsten lamps.

Nitrogen at low pressure disappeared from a bulb containing a tungsten filament at extremely high temperatures (2,800°K.) at a rate independent of its pressure. The rate of disappearance of nitrogen and the loss of weight in the filament showed that one molecule of nitrogen disappeared for every atom of tungsten that evaporated. A brown compound, WN_2, was formed and deposited on the bulb. This decomposed when water vapor was introduced, forming ammonia gas.

"From time to time the question kept arising—how good would a lamp be if it had a perfect vacuum?" Langmuir tells us. "Now, from studies of the character I have described, I began to have an answer. Hydrogen, oxygen, nitrogen, carbon monoxide, and in fact every gas that I introduced, with the exception of water vapor, did not produce blackening of the lamp bulb. The serious blackening that occurred with only small amounts of water vapor depended upon a cyclic reaction in which atomic hydrogen played an essential part. The water-vapor molecules coming in contact with the hot filament produce a volatile oxide of tungsten, and the hydrogen is liberated in atomic form. The volatile oxide deposits on the bulb where it is reduced to the metallic state by the atomic hydrogen, while the water vapor produced returns to the filament and causes the action to be repeated indefinitely. Thus a minute quantity of water vapor may cause a relatively enormous amount of tungsten to be carried to the bulb.

"The question then arose whether the traces of water vapor, which might still exist in a well-exhausted lamp, were responsible for the blackening which limited the life or the efficiency of many of these lamps. We made some tests in which well-made lamps were kept completely immersed in liquid air during their life, so that there could be no possibility of water vapor coming in contact with the filament. The rate of blackening, however, was exactly the same as if no liquid air had been used.

"Having thus proved that the blackening of a well-made lamp was due solely to evaporation, I could conclude with certainty that the life of the lamp would not be appreciably improved even if we would produce a perfect vacuum."

Later experiments based on his theory of heat losses from filaments led Langmuir to filaments coiled in rather tight helices and to bulbs filled with nitrogen instead of the high vacua of early lamps. The result was a substantial increase in the life of his lamps and large increases in their efficiencies as light producers. From his early gas-filled lamps evolved our present high-efficiency incandescent electric lighting.

The basic method employed by Langmuir in arriving at a statement of his problem was the antithesis of Oenslager's. Where Oenslager drew conclusions and built up theories from great numbers of experiments, Langmuir followed Aristotle, and later Bancroft, in setting up hypotheses and then conducting experiments designed to prove or disprove them. Both methods led to clarification of the problem and its ever-clearer statement, essential to solving it.

Clear statement of the problem marks an important advance toward its solution. Not infrequently the mere statement points directly to that end, but most often a lot of concentrated mental effort still remains to be exerted before we can reach it. Let's look next at that process of thinking our way toward a final solution.

CHAPTER 4

Thinking Out the Problem

If you have never played the game of "Twenty Questions," you should try it sometime. Actually, it suggests one of the most powerful tools of research, of sorting out significant facts from a vast accumulation of unorganized data, of finding a needle in a haystack. And that, of course, is most important in any creative thinking, to find the few grains of significance in a vast heap of useless ideas.

There are many ways to play the game, but the common one is to send a member of the party out of the room while the rest agree upon some object for the absent one to guess when he comes back. The guesser is permitted to ask twenty questions, one after the other, that can be answered in either of two ways (yes or no, for instance). The rest of the company must answer truthfully and the guesser is scored on the basis of the number of questions he must ask before he arrives at the answer; the fewer the questions, the higher the score. A simple enough game, but one that employs the basic method of problem solving and research.

If we assume that the questions are so designed that each answer cuts the number of possible solutions in half, then our twenty questions should sort out the single correct answer from something over a million original possibilities. The actual number of possibilities that this process can sort down to one is 1,048,576 (the twentieth power of two). Usually, the questioner can reach the correct answer long before his twenty questions are exhausted. But occasionally, revealing questions become so difficult to devise that after half a dozen or so the guesser either jumps to the answer or gives up.

Perhaps the questions might go like this:

    1. Living or lifeless?

2. Animal or vegetable?
3. Male or female?
4. Heavier than 100 pounds or lighter?
5. Younger than 21 or older?

Our five questions have thrown out nearly 97 per cent of the original possibles, assuming that each answer reduced their number by half.

Thus we have an important method of reducing rapidly the area in which we need to search for the answer to our particular problem. Suppose, for instance, that there are initially as many as a thousand possible answers. Each time we are able to narrow our field of possibilities by half by asking and answering some question, we progressively shrink our area of inquiry by that much. Our first question reduces our possibilities from 1,000 to 500, our second leaves us with only 250, our third brings this down to 125, our fourth leaves only 62.5 possibilities, and our fifth leaves but 31.25 that must still be treated. Clearly our five questions have given us the basis for reducing the original thousand possibilities to a little over 3 per cent of their number (actually 3 1/8 per cent). In other words, our five questions have divided our possibilities by the fifth power of two (thirty-two). If we suppose that each possibility that we faced in the beginning would have needed an experiment before we could otherwise have eliminated it, then our five questions have materially reduced our work load. Furthermore, in the case we have chosen (based upon an original thousand possibilities), if we continue our series of questions with the same effectiveness that we have assumed for the first five, then at the tenth question we would have reduced our original thousand to a single certainty (divide our thousand by 1024, the tenth power of two).

We might note here that this narrowing process is the exact opposite of two traditional applications of the geometric progression based on the increasing powers of two. The ancient story is that an oriental potentate wished to reward the inventor of the game of chess, and promised him anything he might name. Chess's inventor is supposed to have asked for only a few grains of wheat, one for the first square on the chess board and double the number on each succeeding square for the whole sixty-four. He neglected to say that the number of grains of wheat required for the sixth-fourth square alone would be something like 18.45×10^{18}, or eighteen followed by eighteen zeros, a quantity of wheat far larger than any possible world production. The other story of the powers of two has a man suggesting to his friend that the friend deposit a single cent in the bank on the first day of June and double the amount of each day's deposit on each succeeding day for the rest of the month. Sounds innocent enough until you calculate that the deposit for the last day of June would have to be 10.74 millions of dollars!

"We don't solve a technical problem or make an invention in the laboratory. We do these things in our heads. All this laboratory apparatus is simply to help us get an understanding of the problem we are working on," said Charles F. Kettering, the genius behind General Motors' research. Here we have seen how reasoning alone can solve our problems or at least shave them down to a very large extent, requiring that only relatively few of the many original possibilities need to be subjected to the trial of experiments.

To accomplish this requires great mental effort directed in creative channels. Unfortunately, not every person possesses this creative mental ability. Yet this valuable faculty is far more common than is usually supposed, and it can be cultivated and trained. Quite as readily as one's other skills and talents, this too can be sharpened and developed by exercise and practice. We shall look more deeply into that in a subsequent chapter, but for the present let us continue to examine how we may be able to exercise it in solving particular problems. We can do this by reviewing some of the works of masters of research.

No matter what our problem may be, we can be sure someone else before us has approached its solution, or one closely resembling it. The vast accumulation of information, facts, and data in the records of others always provides us with starting material that we can use. Seldom indeed is it necessary for us to begin our search in total darkness. Although this occasionally happens, as we have noted with Edison and Oenslager, for example, these cases are decidedly the exceptions rather than the rule. Both of these investigators, in the cases we have mentioned, had to make many experiments in order to determine what kind of questions, and in what area, they would have to answer before they could begin to ask their "twenty questions." Both of these men, using Sir Francis Bacon's multitudes of experiments in developing a theory, and Langmuir, who in the tradition of Aristotle and Bancroft formed his theory first, could only begin their question game after they had delimited as far as they could the general field of their search. From the development of some kind of a reasonable theory of the problem and its solution, the searcher can at once begin to narrow it down by the method of asking questions and answering them. Sometimes these answers can be drawn from the searcher's experience or from what he has read of the work of others in the same or related fields. But often the question game requires that an experiment be designed to fit specific questions that cannot be answered otherwise. Here the greatest skill and the most careful design, as well as meticulous performance, must go into the experiment. This is manifestly true whether we believe with Sir Francis Bacon and his followers in the infallibility of experimental proof and hasten to discard theories at odds with our observations, or whether we prefer to heed Bancroft's warning against "the misleading experiment" that does not fit with our preconceived theory. Whether we intend to build our theory on our experimental observations, or to discard results that do not conform to our already erected theory, we must perform each experiment with meticulous care, lest it truly mislead us.

In concentrating on the thought process as we have, we have neglected to emphasize what probably is *the* vital characteristic of the scientific method as distinct from our customary habits of thinking. The key is that the data we use in our thinking must be *true,* so far as it is possible for us to determine truths, and they must be expressed to a degree of precision that fits with the general area of our thinking.

Countless examples occur to each of us of being misled by some appearance into believing it to be fact. An old teacher of mine had a favorite way of teaching his pupils not to be misled by appearances. In front of the class he would talk about misleading experiences for a bit and then would apparently change the subject and talk about the chemical properties of alum while holding in his hand a bottle clearly labeled powdered alum. When he had talked about the ability of alum to shrink tissue and pucker up one's mouth, he would stick his finger into the bottle and then into his mouth. Then he would invite the class to learn by experience what the action of alum is, and pass the bottle around. Each student in turn would do the same as the professor apparently had, but, unlike the professor (who maintained a straight face throughout), each one's face would be contorted by the action of the alum on the inside of his mouth and on his tongue. "You see," said the professor, "none of you watched me closely enough. You didn't see that I stuck my index finger into the alum, but my middle finger into my mouth!"

In the same vein was a lecture by the late Frederick E. Breithut, who taught chemistry in New York's City College. Talking to a group of chemical salesmen whom he sought to introduce to the science behind the products they sold, Professor Breithut would discourse at some length about a cigar he held in his hand, an imposing cigar with a bright imposing-looking band on it. The class expected him at any moment to interrupt his lecture about the need to look beyond surface appearances and light up his smoke. But after a few moments, when everyone had seen the imposing cigar, he dropped it on the desk in front of him. It hit with a loud clank, and it was hardly necessary for the professor to explain that it was merely an iron cigar trapped out to look like the real thing!

Simple, these illustrations of the misleading appearance of things, but not at all foolish. For every day each of us encounters numbers of examples of the same misleading appearance at almost every turn. *Only by questioning each bit of data,* each observation, each opinion that comes to us, can we reasonably expect our thinking to lead us to valid and useful conclusions.

With even greater rigor than a trial lawyer, we must exclude from our data all kinds of rumors and hearsay. It is fine to set up guesses, hypotheses if you need a more scientific word, and use these as part of our thinking. Trouble starts only if we confuse such assumptions with facts *before we have been able to prove them.* So long as these guesses are labeled in our thinking for what they are, we can use them to advantage in many situations. Perhaps we may later prove them true and then we can move them out of the nebulous class of assumptions into the realm of fact—*but not until then!* The habit we all have of accepting some rumor or half-truth as fact is at the root of much of the misunderstanding that causes strife in our lives and in our world. If we are to get all the benefit there is in the scientific method as applied to our personal affairs, we must figuratively bite every fact passed to us to be sure that it is the hard metal of coinage and not simply the lead slug of rumor and surmise. At a time like this, in a world torn as ours is by civil strife and riotous behavior, it is easy for any of us to be thrown clear off our figurative rockers by rumors or half-truths that may come to us. We don't have to be misled by them, nor into buying a huge package of corn flakes or detergent half filled with air, when by merely lifting it in comparison with a smaller but heavier one, we can learn what is the true economy.

It is easy too to give ourselves a false sense of the refinement of our data if we express them in terms far more precise than the evidence justifies. For instance, it would be a little ridiculous and quite misleading to express the road distance between New York and Miami as 1,355 miles, 75 feet, 6 inches, when the fact is that for practical purposes the measurement might be anywhere between 1,340 miles and 1,370 miles. If you are a map maker or a surveyor, then you would need a closer value than that, and would hardly go to a road map to get it. On the other hand, if, as seems much more likely, you are simply driving the route in your family car, then you probably could not by the means at your disposal determine the mileage any closer than that, or tell the difference between these values if you tried.

Earlier in this chapter, we thought about the powers of two and expressed the twentieth power of two as 1,048,-576. If this figure had been arrived at using a five-place logarithm table, it would be 1,048,600, and that is quite close enough to the true value for our purposes. That may even be expressed to an unnecessary degree of precision, since the argument in which we used it could be quite as well served had we said that the twentieth power of two is a little greater than a million! You can save yourself great amounts of mental exertion in cases of this kind if you express numbers, for instance, by only the *significant* figures. Thus our twentieth power of two might be best expressed as 1.05 millions, since the figures after the third one are no longer significant for our present purposes. It is all relative. A thousandth part of an inch means nothing in the dimensions of a room, but it can be painfully vital in the height of the filling in a tooth!

Both of these considerations are vital in the practice of the scientific method: clearly differentiating between proved facts and mere assumptions among the data used in our thinking; and continually placing a realistic value on the precision with which we think of quantities and figures in our use of them among our data.

Perhaps this discussion is already leading us too far from our original objective here: to point out the extreme necessity of thinking out our problem until we have an understanding of it that is clear, broad, and deep. Only when we have achieved that kind of lucid knowledge of our objective can we expect to go directly to it. Only the exceptional genius is able to leap over great gaps in his data and see clearly the solution of his problem, the way to soothe the hurt of the thorn in his mind. This is wonderful to behold, but if we examine even this closely we will most likely find that the lightning stroke of genius hit, not a vacant field, but a mind well prepared and ready for the flash of genius to bring it to fruition.

This preparation, essential whether the flash is to strike the mind of a genius or just an ordinary mind like yours or mine, consists essentially in storing in the mind and memory a substantial number of facts and impressions bearing on the principal theme. These stored data may come from: (a) one's own experiences; (b) the experiences of others stored in the accounts they have either recorded in reports or publications, or passed on to us in verbal accounts; (c) dialogues with others singly or in groups; or (d) experiments of our own or others that we have witnessed. In all these cases, the amassed data must be available on call to be brought out and fitted into a pattern that may solve our problem.

John Tyndall, the British physicist (1820–1893) who was professor of natural philosophy and later superintendent at the Royal Institution, expressed it this way: "With accurate experiment and observation to work upon, imagination becomes the architect of physical theory. Newton's passage from a falling apple to a falling moon was an act of the prepared imagination. Out of the facts of chemistry, the constructive imagination of Dalton formed the atomic theory. Davy was richly endowed with the imaginative faculty, while with Faraday its exercise was incessant, preceding, accompanying and guiding his experiments. His strength and fertility as a discoverer are to be referred in great part to the stimulus of his imagination."

The mental process is the vital essence of creativity. Whatever may be one's views on the most effective proportion between observation, reading, and experiment, there can be no avoidance of, or short cut around, the reasoning process of research. This alone can bring cause into proper relation with its effect and lead to the final solution of the problem. Whereas anyone can learn to perform the various physical operations of research, not every mind is capable of the essential original thinking. Yet latent ability to think clearly and originally is far more common than one usually supposes; it is a talent, also, that can be cultivated and trained. Quite as readily as other personal skills, one's mental faculty can be sharpened and strengthened by exercise and practice.

Reduced to its simplest terms, creative mental activity consists of countless trial associations of the several facts until a useful combination is realized, or clearly foreseen. In such trial associations, gaps in data appear and the researcher must resort to the literature or to experiment to supply missing pieces. Not infrequently, you can foresee the outcome of learning some particular bit of information beforehand and you can then guess that the next step will be either of two alternatives, depending on the result of the experiment.

The outstanding example of this guessing and duplicating research was the vast program of both research and development which led to the atomic bomb. At every juncture, the outcome of the next step was guessed and the subsequent step undertaken at once. This next step was always designed to answer the next question, whichever way the immediate investigation pointed. Time was always pressing and all the links in the chains of both research and development were forged simultaneously. The strange and fascinating story of how the various pairs of alternatives proved out is sketched, but not fully told, in the official Smyth Report, which everyone should read thoughtfully, and profitably.

Obviously, one's ability to form vast numbers of mental associations depends upon natural aptitude; but also vital is one's quickness of mind, which can be developed and greatly enhanced by practice. Thus it is that original thinkers and research workers, particularly the most successful ones, are inveterate puzzle solvers. They spend their leisure time at some pastime requiring the same kind of skill as their daily occupations. Such hobbies as chess, bridge, cryptography, decipering Mayan inscriptions, reading or writing detective stories, and the many other pursuits requiring intense mental effort find their most enthusiastic devotees among successful research workers. So closely does solving puzzles resemble research in its mental requirements that personnel departments and research directors often use puzzles of one kind or another as part of the tests given applicants to determine their fitness for research positions. These puzzles may be part of, or supplement, more orthodox psychological tests. One type that requires a high degree of associative skill and mental quickness gives the solver a number of apparently unrelated facts to reassemble to give a true picture of a certain situation, wherein the similarity to research problems is greater than appears on the surface. (The Problem of the Cigarette-Smoking Poker Players, for instance.)

Far more often than not, the data gathered in the early stages of a research appear disperse and incomplete. Fortunately for those of us whose minds are baffled by such fragmentary and disordered data, a few more facts gathered experimentally may complete the picture, or bring it into some kind of focus. Fortunately, too, in neither pursuit is there any prohibition against assuming an answer on the basis of any available facts and then subjecting it to

The Problem of the
Cigarette-Smoking Poker Players

Five men are playing poker and each had a different number of a different brand of cigarettes at the time the game started. The names of the men are:

Brown, Perkins, Reilly, Turner, and Jones.

The five brands of cigarettes are:

Luckies, Raleighs, Camels, Old Golds, and Chesterfields.

The numbers of cigarettes at the beginning are:

20, 15, 8, 6, and 3.

In no case is the order of the words above significant.

At a given time:

1. Perkins asks for three cards.
2. Reilly has smoked half of his original supply, or one less than Turner.
3. The Chesterfield smoker originally had as many more, half as many more, and 2½ more cigarettes than he has now.
4. The man who draws to an inside straight absent-mindedly lights the tipped end of his fifth cigarette.
5. The man who smokes Luckies has smoked two more than anyone else, including Perkins.
6. Brown drew as many aces as he had cigarettes.
7. No one has smoked all his cigarettes.
8. The Camel smoker asks Jones to pass Brown's matches.

N.B. Only Raleighs had a cork tip at the time of the game.

The Problem: How many cigarettes did each man have originally and what is each man's brand?

See page 44 for solution.

See page 44 for solution.

* * *

THE PROBLEM OF THE
CIGARETTE-SMOKING POKER PLAYERS

20	15	8	6	3		LUCKIES	RALEIGHS	CAMELS	OLD GOLDS	CHESTERFIELDS
x	x	x	x		BROWN	x	x	x		x
x		x	x	x	PERKINS	x	x	x	x	
x	x		x	x	REILLY	x	x		x	x
x	x	x		x	TURNER	x		x	x	x
	x	x	x	x	JONES		x	x	x	x

The solution of this puzzle has often been used by prospective employers as a rough index of ability in thinking out problems. An active, associative mind should be able to solve it in one to two hours, the time required being a suggestion of how quickly the mind functions.

Everyone will have his own method of solving it. I prefer to start with the given fact that only Raleigh cigarettes of the brands named had two ends that were at that time different. Statement 4 gives us two facts: a. the Raleigh smoker had more than five cigarettes at the beginning; b. he drew one card (to an inside straight). Statement 1 rules out Perkins as the Raleigh smoker (he drew three cards) and statement 5 rules him out as the smoker of Luckies. And so on through the series of statement and the conclusions you can draw from them. Conveniently the conclusions can be entered on a diagram such as this one and, as they accumulate, all possibilities except the right ones are ruled out!

the test of fitting with the other facts. Indeed, no better method can be applied to the usual problems of either research or puzzledom.

The successive steps in the solution of any problem follow the pattern commonly described for promoting original thought. The steps are:

(1) Accumulate all possible facts bearing upon the problem in hand. Study them and impress them on the mind.

(2) Digest and synthesize these facts into a solution, either complete and final, or interim and representing a stage of progress toward the ultimate solution. Obviously, few problems can be solved at one trial and hence piecemeal solutions are the rule.

(3) Repeat these steps alternately as often as necessary, with each repetition appropriately modifying the operation to take into account each bit of progress, however small, that has been made before.

It is hardly necessary to present any arguments for bringing to bear upon the problem each fact that can be mustered; the mind needs raw material to keep going and facts are the raw material of research. Thus we have a pattern of thinking things out that must, for most of us, serve instead of the genius we do not possess. Fortunately, the pattern works.

There are several ways that each of us can increase his research effectiveness. These include a number of rather obvious rules that are so simple and common-sense that they seem trite and hence are neglected. But if you will examine the methods of the most successful researchers you are likely to find that a great deal of the "genius" that is recognized after success is achieved, actually is careful following of a few basic rules:

1. Be sure your problem is stated in terms that make its solution possible for you. Usually that means that you must divide it into small bits that you can handle, instead of tackling the whole problem at once.

Perhaps you cannot with your natural talents, the facilities that you can command, and the time allotted to you solve the big problem, but you certainly can nibble at it by concentrating on parts of it.

2. Concentrate on a small area and learn all there is to know about that small bit. In order to make up the new combinations that are the objectives of research, your subconscious mind cannot use facts that have not been fed to it. But it can do wonders for you if you keep it supplied with factual raw material.

3. Be methodical in collecting, sorting, and recording facts. Nothing could be more discouraging than to have your patent awarded to someone else who could prove the dates of his experiments from good records, but you could not. Whether your data come from the library or the laboratory, be sure you keep good records so that when your present theory proves fruitless you can re-examine your data to form a new theory.

4. Never be so busy that you take no time to think. Sometimes a few minutes of thinking of something else, or of just plain daydreaming, will lead you to relations that no amount of continuous concentration will reveal. Of course, daydreaming can be easily overdone!

5. Often it helps to get a totally different point of view on your problem by discussing it with a colleague or by reading in a different but related field. Often some quite simple concept in physics or botany may suggest the key to a hopeless chemical maze, or vice versa.

These form an excellent pattern to make our research activities more effective.

Having thus set up what may be thought of as a pattern for genius, let us be careful that we do not blind ourselves to the existence of this extremely rare and precious talent. Rather, let us think that the patterns we are discussing tend to help less gifted minds to imitate genius and so to accomplish something that might, by the effectiveness of its very mass, accomplish more than a rare genius can. Clearly, the key to the whole matter consists in our ability (or lack of it) to use whatever talent we may possess to the best advantage. This we can only do if the raw material we supply to our minds consists of true and trustworthy facts. Let us look into the kinds of facts and data that are available to us in a scientific sense, that are the raw material for our best thinking.

CHAPTER 5

Is That a Fact?

If there is any one thing that characterizes the scientific method, it is relentless insistence on proving the truth of every bit of information before it is considered fact. We have touched on this idea briefly in the preceding chapter, but it is so important that we must think further about it. Indeed, this insistence on proof and provability is so essential to scientific thinking that people generally have come to speak of any idea or observation that has been meticulously proved true as being a "scientific fact." The term "scientific" has come to be synonymous with the highest degree of truth in most people's thinking. This is no accident. Rather, it recognizes that truth and honesty must characterize all scientific activity.

Clearly, then, the most careful scrutiny of assembled facts and presumed facts is vital to the practice of our scientific method. It is obviously futile and foolish to embark upon an extended train of reasoning on the basis of any data that are not the most reliable that can be had, or that have not been carefully proved. If there is anything uncertain about our premise, then any structure of reasoning erected upon it must necessarily be unstable and insecure. The step-by-painstaking-step nature of scientific progress could never be realized unless each step had been subjected to the most rigorous proof.

This line of reasoning would seem to exclude hypotheses (guesses or suppositions set up to be proved or disproved), but obviously it does not. Quite the contrary. Suppositions that are clearly recognized for what they are provide a most effective way for science to progress. So long as you do not confuse a guess with proved fact, so long as you recognize the uncertainty of a theory, it can be a highly useful tool. Even though the guess may be headed in the wrong direction, it can serve a highly useful purpose. We have noted in the preceding chapter the case of the iron cigar, about which appearances built up a false theory in the observers' minds, and that of the switching of fingers inserted into the bottle of powdered alum. If the deceptive theory in each of these cases served no other useful purpose, it at least emphasized the need for careful observation of *all* facts before accepting them as true. Thus following a false theory, hoping to prove it true, can be highly fruitful. The classic example was the extremely precise and accurate determination of atomic weights by the Belgian chemist, Jean Servais Stas, who set out in the nineteenth century to prove that all atoms must possess relative weights that are precise whole-number multiples of the atomic weight of hydrogen. Stas performed the most exacting measurements of atomic weights and ultimately his results proved conclusively that his original theory was quite definitely false! So we can state a reasonable rule: don't discard a good theory until you have proved it false; but neither accept as true a theory that has not been proved.

In any case, either to form a theory or to prove it, you must accumulate facts. We have already pointed out that these may come from experience (your own or someone's else), from written or published papers, books and reports, or from experiments designed and performed to prove or disprove a particular point. Perhaps the most successful procedure is to accumulate from every available source all facts that seem to bear on the immediate problem and then to organize these into some kind of a unified picture or theory. Having thus reached a theory of the solution to the problem, we then come to the experiments that will either prove or disprove the theory.

We might think of the freshly gathered facts as somewhat like a forkful of hay with the grass blades and stems matted together and pointing in every direction. Some of the grass blades in the mass are useful but many of the stems are not, just as your assembled mass of information and data will include both useful and valueless and misleading statements. Some of the discards will be false; some, inaccurate; some, lacking in precision; and others simply have no bearing on our particular problem. But all must be examined, some must be checked, and some must finally be adopted to form at least a theory pointing toward, if not actually being, the final answer to the problem.

Two attributes of our data bear essentially on their acceptability as true and factual: the precision of the measurements on which they are based, and the accuracy with which these observations were made. We must understand clearly the difference between precision and accuracy in the scientific sense. Precision has to do with the nature of a measurement and the standard by which it is determined. On the other hand, accuracy is primarily involved with the care employed in making the measurement. A micrometer that measures to the hundredth of a millimeter or to a thousandth of an inch is an instrument of greater precision than a yardstick or a meter rule, for instance. Yet it is possible by using care in one's observations to make accurate measurements with any of these—or carelessly inaccurate ones. Similarly, the degree of precision of weighings with the analytical balance in the laboratory can be as great as one tenth of a milligram in a load of 100 grams. That is one part in a million and could be translated into the equivalent of three or four aspirin tablets in a ton of coal, for instance. No one needs to weigh a ton of coal that closely, but scientific work often requires such precision, and it is far easier to drop from a high degree of precision to a lower one than it is to go the other way. A favorite stunt to impress a visitor to the laboratory with the extreme sensitivity of our weighings used to be to have him write his name with a pencil on a previously weighed piece of paper and then to weigh it again to give him the weight of his signature, or the weight of his name!

A competent weighmaster might reach his practical limit of accuracy if his weight was within a few pounds, say two to ten, of the exact weight of the coal. That is the practical limit of precision of the scale he would use. But for scientific purposes, the greater precision of one part per million in weighings provides the scientist with just that much greater assurance in using the data so obtained.

Indeed, all the operations of the scientific laboratory are designed to provide data of the greatest precision by using instruments of the highest sensitivity. The extreme penetration of the electron microscope, for example, enables one to extend his vision far down into the realm of the infinitely small and far beyond the range of a microscope employing visible, or even ultraviolet, light. Viewed through a light microscope at even its greatest useful magnification (about 1,000X), many extremely fine powders are not resolved into their individual tiny particles, but rather appear as indistinct groups of particles. On the other hand, the far greater resolving power of the electron beam (100,000X or even more) allows the individual particles of such material as kaolin clay and precipitated chalk to be clearly seen and differentiated. Electron micrographs at about 45,000X show why kaolin, made up of thin platelets that easily slip on one another, has a greasy feel, and why chalk, revealed as branching and intertwined crystals, proves to be abrasive and feels that way between your fingers.

Another powerful tool of the chemical laboratory is the ultraviolet spectrograph. Metals produce characteristic lines in the spectra in the ultraviolet region when heated to incandescent temperatures in an electric arc. The quantity necessary to produce the characteristic lines is extremely small. For example, if a silver spoon is merely *dipped* into a cup of freshly brewed coffee that is then poured out of the cup, evaporated to dryness, and then burned in an electric arc, the ultraviolet spectrum will show two lines characteristic of silver. But there is no need to fear your silverware will disappear in your coffee—calculation shows that you could safely stir your coffee with an average sterling silver spoon daily for some 1,700 years before the loss of silver would be great enough to be serious!

With these and other penetrating instruments to help us gather facts and with vast libraries of observations by others at our command, the amount of information available to us on almost any imaginable subject is tremendous. The important problem often facing the researcher is the task of bringing order out of the chaos of too much information, of co-ordinating the various data into a coherent picture, rejecting nonpertinent material and organizing the significant remainder into a unified whole that suggests a way to proceed. Sometimes a pattern becomes obvious from a mere inspection of available data, but often one becomes only more confused by studying their divergence. Some geniuses are able to digest masses of data mentally and come up with co-ordinating patterns, but more often confusion, rather than order, grows when ordinary mortals attempt it.

When one has become thoroughly confused by too much patternless information, a way out can often be found by plotting values and then fairing a curve through the plotted points. This procedure immediately shows up values that are far out of line and usually reveals "pointing fingers" that suggest a way to go. At times, data that refuse to fit together when plotted on straight rectangular co-ordinate paper can be made to yield when plotted on logarithmic or semi-logarithmic paper, which allows one to plot values directly as the logarithms of one or both variables. This, of course, assumes that data have been reduced to numerical values.

Even if these plots fail to yield logical patterns, statistical treatments employing the laws of probability and of mean variation, among others, may help to sort out the true from the false. Many splendid texts describe statistical methods, but two have been especially useful to me. A Pelican paperback, *Facts from Figures* by M. J. Moroney, discusses in detail a variety of mathematical and statistical techniques that are most helpful in getting order out of chaotic assemblies of data. Perhaps more specifically valuable to the creative thinker is *Methods of Operations Research* by Philip M. Morse and George E. Kimball, which discusses methods of arriving at executive decisions from data that may not be as complete as one might wish. A more recent work is *Great Ideas of Operations Research* by Jagjit Singh, published by Dover in 1968.

Here we are in the field where modern computers are extremely valuable. We hear a great deal about the magical powers of computers, with their vast ability to accept, store, and co-ordinate data. Calculations that might take months or even years (if indeed they could be accomplished by men at all) can be performed by modern electronic computers in seconds. Furthermore, the intricate abstruse calculations involved in plotting the courses of our artificial satellites in outer space entail enormous numbers of the most intricate equations that must be calculated to almost unbelievable precision; yet these operations can be performed by electronic means with scarcely credible swiftness, faster by far than human abilities can write down the results! Here lies the enormous value of these instruments—in making calculations of the greatest intricacy and in staggering numbers that are scarcely within the power of even teams of our best mathematicians. Yet these are repetitive tasks—the drudgery of science, shall we say —that require human brains and inspiration to set them going. It is not yet possible to imagine a machine that can take the place of the far greater intricacy of the human brain and its ability to imagine and create.

No amount of mechanical or electronic help has yet been found to substitute for the creative function of the human brain. Nor is it likely that anything of the kind will be dis-

covered. Creative imaginations, rare as these seem sometimes to be, are still quite irreplaceable. In other words,
let us use our minds as creatively as we can. If we are
to do that, then we must look into how the mind functions
and what we can do to encourage and stimulate it—as we
shall do in the next chapter.

CHAPTER 6

We Think Out the Solution

Back in the very early days of this twentieth century, our country was plagued by a rash of food faddists. From today's point of view, the common diet of that day was far short of what later findings in nutrition showed to be optimum; but also, the gropings of the food faddists were very little, if any, better in leading us to become better people through selecting our diet. Indeed, one school, taking a particular dislike to heavy, difficultly digestible foods, urged more vegetables and less meat, peanut butter instead of pork roasts. Their slogan was: "Tell me what you eat, and I'll tell you what you are!" (To which the impudent are said to have replied: "Well, anyway, I'd rather be a pig than a peanut!") The implication was that through dietary control the faddist had somehow come near the high point of development that has been instinctive with honeybees. Bees feed certain of their larvae a special "royal jelly" to insure that they develop into queens, and give others appropriate food to enable them to develop into workers or drones in a proportion required by the hive's economy. We too can improve the physique of our young by diet, but we are far short of the bees' dramatic accomplishment.

We are still far behind the hopes of the food faddists and the instinctive practices of the bees in our ability to precondition our young to be creative geniuses, even though the need for creativity today seems overwhelming. Our most advanced psychologists are still uncertain how we might create creativity in an uncreative subject, but at least they are able to suggest conditions that favor development of this enormously valuable faculty and talent. Indeed, you needn't be radical to see our whole educational program as designed to encourage developing minds and to bring out and nurture every spark of creativity latent in any pupil. At one time, education may have resembled nothing so much as an overloaded buffet where the student was encouraged to overeat of everything that at the moment appealed to him. Today, the healthy tendency is to turn our intellectual buffet more and more into a kind of training table that will give pupils a mental diet that will do for their minds somewhat the same thing that the selected foods of the training table do for our athletes' bodies.

Our psychologists, psychiatrists, and others concerned with people's minds have progressed enormously in recent decades in their ability to detect, define, treat, and cure mental disorders. Similarly, they are able to learn much of the hidden past history of a disturbed mind and the causes of its disturbance by studying its present state. Soon, we hope, they may be able to precondition healthy, developing minds into creative channels with far more assurance than any or all of our techniques can do today. The process of "brainwashing," for example, has proved how possible it is to undermine a person's thinking mechanism and even change his personality; soon, hopefully, we should be equally able to build or remodel minds for creativity.

What we have been considering in preceding chapters are the mechanics of the creative art. For it is an art, not yet grown up into a science. It will be useful now to attempt to find method in it. If we inquire of creative people about how they are creative, what the conditions are for creation, and how they establish and utilize these conditions, we shall hear almost as many answers as there are people questioned. Washington Platt, of the Borden Company, and Ross A. Baker, of the College of the City of New York, did just that some years ago; they addressed a questionnaire to some fourteen hundred creative scientists in a variety of fields and then assembled the answers, seeking a clear pattern of creativity. The pattern is there, of course, but its outlines and individual parts are in less than clear focus—more an impressionistic painting than a blueprint—since the experiences described happened to such a diversity of people under what appeared superficially to be the most completely unordered circumstances. Platt and Baker directed their questions primarily to scientists of several disciplines, but the responses they received and the pattern they developed from them might apply as well to poetry, or painting, or music, or any other creative activity. The diversity of their data seems to lead to results less than conclusive, possibly because they have sought to be scientifically exact about phenomena that are themselves not exactly determinable. If, on the other hand, we use their findings in a way that is in keeping with their low precision and combine these with observations of many other creators in many fields, perhaps we shall find in them useful ideas that will help us to sharpen our own creative faculties.

Since creativity is essentially a mental process, it behooves us to examine as closely as we can the way our minds operate and how they can be stimulated to produce ideas. We have looked briefly into the scientific method in preceding chapters and have seen how we pass from one proved and tested step to the next in reaching out from what we know into a region of the unknown. We have seen how one proved fact added to another enables us gradually to work our way along a narrow path toward our hoped-for goal. And how each step we take toward our objective gradually narrows the area of our ignorance about it until finally we are able to see our way clearly.

Previously, we have noted the several steps of creativity: sensing a problem; stating the problem; assembling data to use in forming a solution; choosing and combining data into a solution; and finally testing our suggestion to prove whether it is a solution or not. All of these steps are important, but at present we shall direct our special attention to the third and fourth steps—assembling facts and data, and correlating these to synthesize a tentative solution from them.

Let us be clear in our thinking: these several steps are equally important, no matter what the nature of our problem may be. While the nature of our particular problem will color our view and shift our vantage point for thinking about any fact, still, our accumulation of data must be *the* important step toward the creative action we hope to take.

Suppose that a number of creative people look at a sunrise. A poet might see in it: the end, the death, of darkness; the coloring of the dark blue velvet of the sky with the vivid colors that herald the sun; the disappearance of the bright stars, the silver buttons strewn on the dark waistcoat of the night sky; the birth of a new day of hope and promise; the opportunity for making a new start toward life's goals. A navigator's interest would center around that brief interval of time when he can discern the distant horizon and at the same time see the stars he needs to fix his position on the trackless ocean. To a farmer, dawn is the time when he must feed and care for his animals, and lay out the day's chores for his laborers. The sleepyhead will resent the growing light of the new day because it interferes with his continuing slumbers. A hunter in his blind may wait breathlessly for the ducks to fly. A painter will seek new significance in the patterns and colors of sky and clouds at this turning point between darkness and light. A musician may hear notes, chords, and tones in the sounds of an awakening world that he can weave into new melodies. A photographer would wait for the exact moment when the strengthening light had penetrated just far enough into the shadows to bring out the beauty he sees in some common object or scene. We could go on and on describing the multitudes of ways different people might view even so commonplace a phenomenon as the daily rising of the sun. But these examples suggest the various guises in which we might clothe even that simple oft-repeated event.

Without an accumulation of facts, observations, sensations, impressions, as we have noted before, we have nothing to put together into our new thought, our creative solution. Furthermore, our store of raw material for our thinking must be orderly so that we can call forth any bit of it when we need it and place it as needed in the pattern of our thought to fill a gap in the picture we are creating. This is not to deny that some unordered minds are able to create novel combinations, but rather that the chance of their being able to do so on demand is far less than if their thinking were reasonably organized.

The trunk of a tree, drawing nourishment from roots reaching an extended area, corresponds to the stored and trained mind that draws from the greatest variety of sources to nourish the tree of its thoughts which then branches out into the leaves and fruit of accomplishment by utilizing its acquired powers.

Thought proceeds in chain fashion through a series of associations of ideas. Progression from one idea or mental picture to the next in the chain is ordinarily so swift that a succession of ideas will have flashed through the mind in the smallest conscious interval of time. A sudden interruption of this progression sometimes yields a reasonable picture, but, more often, any single idea out of context seems unrelated to what has gone before and what comes after. The uncontrolled flash of images in this fashion follows a pattern based on the mind's history and the interruption of the chain at intervals provides the psychoanalyst with data from which to reconstruct this history. While the series of associations by any mind is individual and characteristic of that mind, psychologists are able to discern and distinguish important broad classes of mental reactions and aptitudes.

Just as the past history of a mind can be reconstructed from its present reactions, so, too, can its present or future reactions be foreshadowed by its training and experience. It is quite difficult, even impossible, for a mind ignorant of the multiplication table, for instance, to associate or relate to each other the numbers two and four. Further mathematical training will permit sixteen to be readily associated with two and four as the fourth power of two or the second power of four, for example, but this is impossible to one who knows only multiplication. The trained mind thus achieves an enlarged number of methods of associating ideas from the greater variety of the things, situations, and relationships familiar to it. The process of training itself, particularly that of learning new facts, gives the mind practice in relating ideas, because only by association can it retain usefully what it learns. Thus, early in the ordinary processes of education, teachers learn whether or not a particular mind possesses an ability to associate ideas readily. If the student possesses this faculty, education sharpens and strengthens it, and at the same time provides it with material.

Viewed in this light, the entire process of education can be considered as leading toward creativity as its ultimate goal. Not that it must necessarily reach the goal of easy creativity; rather, that it leads the student as far along that path as his abilities and inclinations permit. Nor are long years of education in every case necessary prerequisites to original thinking. That is manifestly so, since brilliant associations of ideas into inventions of profound significance have been the apparently fortuitous products of unschooled minds.

While such things can happen, and do, the chance that they will is slender and tenuous in the extreme. One can not reasonably rely upon the ultimate occurrence of an improbable event. As the training of a mind expands, so too does the probability rise that it will be able to achieve useful new associations of ideas and also that it will be able to solve a particular problem.

Henri Poincaré, great French mathematician and physicist, expanded the idea: "An isolated fact can be observed by all eyes; by those of the ordinary person as well as of the wise. But it is the true physicist alone who may see the bond which unites several facts among which the relationship is important, though obscure. The story of Newton's apple is probably not true, but it is symbolical; so let us think of it as true. Well, we must believe that many before Newton had seen apples fall, but they made no deduction. Facts are sterile until there are minds capable of choosing between them and discerning those which conceal something and recognizing that which is concealed; minds which under the bare fact see the soul of the fact."

Three important sources of facts are at the command of the researcher: experience, observation, and experiment.

Within the term "experience," we include any fact available from the past: one's own personal experience, and other data from the tremendous wealth of the experiences of others treasured in books, pamphlets, and reports. Nor should we overlook the bits gathered from personal contacts with other workers, often our most valuable helps.

Observation performs a vital function when the conditions governing an event are beyond immediate control. Astronomical investigations and many, if not all, researches into geological, biological, and genetic subjects, for example, permit the researcher to exercise only negligible control over the events he studies. He must, therefore, use all his powers to observe every factor and every variable affecting his particular problem.

Experiment acquires value only when pertinent data are completely observed and significant conditions are controlled to the extent that they may affect the result.

The order of mentioning experience, observation, and experiment, the essential sources of facts, is purely fortuitous and is not intended to establish an order of importance of these three sources. Rather, they are, and should be, cognate in the researcher's mind, to be consulted whenever and however circumstances may dictate. Furthermore, in establishing equal values for these several sources of facts, it is essential also to recognize that all are equally likely to prove misleading. No other experience has been acquired by anyone under exactly the circumstances of the particular search in hand. No other observer or experimenter has worked to exactly present specifications. Even the experiments one designs and performs for oneself with the utmost care are quite as likely to mislead as to guide the reasoning processes.

The accumulation of facts by one or all of these methods obviously must follow the pattern that is most acceptable to the person who is to use the facts, and the method that is best adapted to his problem. Long and detailed searches of the literature may be quite unnecessary if we discover early that no such published information exists, or if a brief search turns up material of such pertinence and value that immediate recourse to experiment is needed to test the application of the findings to the present problem. This might very well be the discovery in the literature of exactly the data needed. Observation may be impractical in any particular case (such, for instance, as seeing a process operating in a competitor's plant), and thus the prospective observer is thrown back upon his own resources of experiment and imagination to reach a useful conclusion.

The great volume of literature currently available on practically every imaginable subject encourages one to initiate, and even complete, a research in the library. Our scientific forebears had no such convenient help at hand, but always had to begin by formulating theories of their own and testing them by experiments designed for the purpose. Both methods are just as useful today. Leonardo da Vinci, great artist-engineer-scientist of fifteenth-century Italy, stated his basic creative method thus:

"In treating any particular subject I would first of all make some experiments, because my design is first to refer to experiments and then to demonstrate why bodies are constrained to act in such a manner. This is the method we ought to follow in investigating the phenomena of Nature. Theory is the general, experiments are the soldiers. Experiment is the interpreter of the artifices of Nature. It is never wrong; but our judgment is sometimes deceived because we are expecting results which experiment refuses to give. We must consult experiment and vary the circumstances, till we have deduced general laws, for it alone can furnish us with them."

And Leonardo's personal success in widely diverse fields attests the value of his philosophy.

Francis Bacon, the great advocate of the experimental method, freely criticized those who, as was the fashion in his day and before, relied wholly on speculation:

"For all those who before me have applied themselves to the invention of arts have but cast a glance or two upon facts and examples and experience, and straightway proceeded, as if invention were nothing more than an exercise of thought, to invoke their own spirits to give them oracles. I, on the contrary, dwelling purely and constantly among the facts of nature, withdraw my intellect from them no further than may suffice to let the images and rays of natural objects meet in a point, as they do in the sense of vision; whence it follows that the strength and excellency of the wit has but little to do in the matter. . . .

"Now what the sciences stand in need of is a form of induction which shall analyse experience and take it to pieces, and by a due process of exclusion and rejection lead to an inevitable conclusion. And if that ordinary mode of judgment practised by the logicians was so laborious, and found exercise for such great wits, how much more labour must we be prepared to bestow upon this other, which is extracted not merely out of the depths of the mind, but out of the very bowels of nature. . . .

"If we begin with certainties, we shall end in doubts; but if we begin with doubts, and are patient in them, we shall end in certainties."

We have already noted that the view which Bacon thus vigorously attacked, that the method of pure logic scarcely influenced by experiment, still functions usefully. But so too does Bacon's! Let us, however, look upon these differences as signs of mental health and vigor and not as establishing one or the other as unalterable law to which we must constantly and consistently adhere under all circumstances. We have already examined the two in an earlier chapter, but it remains to illustrate and to clarify their applications.

Whatever one may be bent upon doing, the necessity of providing oneself with a bountiful supply of facts and experience at the outset is constant. Thomas Hobbes, the seventeenth-century English philosopher, looked at the problem of original thinking from a point of view that appears somewhat archaic to modern eyes, but nonetheless, his conclusions are completely sound today. If, for "prophecy," one reads "invention," or even "the advancement of science," the following excerpt from his "Of Man" becomes highly pertinent:

"The best prophet naturally is the best guesser; and the best guesser, he that is most versed and studied in the matters he guesses at, for he hath most 'signs' to guess by.

"A 'sign' is the event antecedent, of the consequent; and, contrarily, the consequent of the antecedent, when the like consequences have been observed before; and the oftener they have been observed, the less uncertain is the sign. And therefore he that has most experience in any kind of business has most signs whereby to guess at the future time, and consequently is the most prudent; and so much more prudent than he that is new in that kind of business as not to be equalled by any advantage of natural and extemporary wit; though perhaps many young men think the contrary."

Graham Wallas continues this thought into the second stage of research:

"The educated man has learnt, and can voluntarily or habitually follow out, rules as to the order in which he shall direct his attention to the successive elements in a problem. Hobbes referred to this fact when in the *Leviathan* he described 'regulated thought' and contrasted it with that 'wild ranging of the mind' which occurs when the thought-process is undirected. Regulated thought is, he says, a 'seeking.' 'Sometimes,' for instance, 'a man seeks what he has lost. . . . Sometimes a man knows a place determinate, within the compass whereof he is to seek; and then his thoughts run over all the parts thereof, in the same manner as one would sweep a room to find a jewel; or as a spaniel ranges the field till he finds a scent; or as a man should run over the alphabet, to start a rhyme.' A spaniel with the brain of an educated human being could not, by a direct effort of will, scent a partridge in a distant part of the field. But he could so 'quarter' the field by a preliminary voluntary arrangement that the less-voluntary process of smelling would be given every chance of successfully taking place."

Perhaps it is less than complimentary to compare our great researchers to a spaniel, but nevertheless, the figurative quartering of the field in search of facts, and clues to connect them, fits precisely with the mental pattern of every successful researcher.

Whenever and however one obtains his basic facts, each fact must be suspect to the researcher until its validity has been conclusively proved. Too often we assume that some mere notion is a true fact simply because someone else before us has said so. Our habitual discarding of the livers of animals, the bran of wheat, and the peelings of potatoes required the most extensive investigations into nutrition, backed by tremendous publicity, and enforced by the regimentation of a world war to prove and to correct our wasteful habits. Research cannot succeed when its progress is hampered by cherished ideas that are not submitted to test and proof.

J. B. A. Dumas, eminent French organic chemist of the nineteenth century, emphasized differences between events observed and deliberately planned experiments. Said he:

"The art of observation and that of experimentation are distinct. In the first case, the fact may either proceed from logical reasons or be mere good fortune; it is sufficient to have some penetration and the sense of truth in order to profit by it. But the art of experimentation leads from the first to the last link of the chain, without hesitation and without a blank, making successive use of Reason, which suggests an alternative, and of Experience, which decides on it, until, starting from a faint glimmer, the full blaze of light is reached."

An astoundingly high percentage of industrial research problems have yielded to these processes of learning and marshaling facts and then drawing conclusions from them. Not infrequently the process is cyclic, and requires several cycles of search, experiment, and co-ordination of the findings. Usually one is able thus to simplify the problem in successive stages until the final solution may even become obvious and inescapable.

Sometimes that does not happen. The cycle fails to simplify the problem or to narrow the area in which a solution might reasonably be sought. Something more is necessary. Original thinking only can bridge the gap and that sometimes requires a complete change of procedure. Psychologists tell us that what the conscious mind cannot or will not do is sometimes easy for the subconscious mind. They point out that great numbers of discoveries, inventions, and developments spring directly from the seeming inspiration which characterizes the successful working of the subconscious mind. Furthermore, the method of bringing this invaluable agency into action is simple and quite well understood. It consists of three steps. Two of these will already have been taken by the research worker before he faces a blank wall after several cycles of the processes described above. The first step is to charge the mind with all the information bearing on the subject of the search that one can lay his hands upon. The second grows logically from that and consists in collating and co-ordinating the accumulated information as far as, and in every way, possible. It is important to utilize all sources of raw material—experience, literature, and experiment—in the accumulating process and to place no limitations as to practicability upon the patterns into which this material may be grouped. Free association, the psychologists call it; brainstorming is the advertising man's term. It is usually impossible to predict practicability surely; and easy to prove it later.

This condition of free association of ideas is usually impractical to realize in conscious thinking because the conscious mind tends always to work in cycles, to wear grooves of repetitive thinking and to follow them endlessly. That cyclic following of worn ruts of thought builds up to the insurmountable wall that separates us from our objectives and defeats our efforts to get ahead. Presumably, the value of our subconscious minds lies in their freedom from ruts, or in their ability to rise above them and to reach conclusions impossible for rut-bound thought.

When given an opportunity, the subconscious mind is capable of the most amazing feats and in the end presents our conscious mind with a flash of inspiration, the "flash of genius" of the patent law, with minimum apparent effort. The process of final inspiration resembles nothing so much as the charging of an electrical condenser. Toward the end, the rate of charging becomes extremely slow, but ultimately it builds up a charge great enough to overcome the resistance of the system in a lightninglike flash. The first part of the charge may be imparted at whatever speed the individual mind finds adaptable and in ordinary course this rapidly imparted charge alone may raise the potential to the point of rupture. Thus, in our ordinary thinking, we reach the mental potential needed for the conclusion by quite ordinary processes. When, however, our usual faculties are unable to reach the mental potential required to solve some intricate or abstruse situation, we can utilize to advantage the power of our subconscious minds to add by tiny increments the last tiny part of the charge needed to achieve the "flash of genius."

The analogy between original thinking and building up an electrical potential is somewhat closer than appears at first blush. As we have noted, the thinking process consists basically in fitting together enormous numbers of combinations of elements in the mind until the whole presents a satisfactory overall pattern, which is the solution to the problem. Multitudes of indications must finally point in the same direction. In an electrical sense, the gross charge on a body can be considered to be built up by the arrangement of innumerable tiny charges of the magnitude of those on electrons. In both cases, the result is achieved by aligning great numbers of infinitesimal forces (mental or electrical) in such a way that the resultant of their operation is the sum of all of them.

Just as electrical charges can only be built up to great magnitude by preventing any of the accumulating charges from leaking away, so the exercise of great mental power requires that the process be allowed to proceed without interruption or mental disturbance. A state of mental insulation that fosters the mind's subconscious activity is most easily achieved by relaxing mental tensions. This need not require physical isolation. The circumstances conducive to this state differ for different individuals, but all have in common the idea of blocking out annoying and disturbing thoughts and inducing mental relaxation by whatever method may be individually most effective.

Sometimes a state of mental rest is created by the simple process of isolation, or by physical rest, or by some kind of activity, either mental or physical, that is quite different from those of every day. While the greatest variety of circumstances have been credited by various individuals with heightening their mental powers, these have only two aspects in common: relaxation of mental

tensions and exclusion of irritating and disturbing extraneous thoughts.

The circumstances of revelation and inspiration possess
astonishing variety. Platt and Baker made a particular
study of the subject of original thinking among research
men, as we have noted before, and reported their findings in the *Journal of Chemical Education* in 1931 (Volume 8, page 1969). Their study revealed cases where the
requisite degree of mental insulation was achieved by such
varied acts as: walking briskly downtown in anticipation
of a steak dinner; riding a train before dawn; resting and
loafing on the beach; sitting at a desk idly thinking of
other matters; dodging through automobile traffic; awakening in the morning; dressing after a swim in the ocean;
dozing after a hard day's work; sitting in church; shaving;
riding in an automobile; listening to fine music; and many
others equally various.

On this subject, Barrett Wendell, of Harvard University,
said: "My method of clearing my ideas is by no means
the only one. I have known people who could do it best by
talking; by putting somebody else in a comfortable chair
and making him listen to their efforts to discover what they
really think. I have known others who could really do best
by sitting still and pondering in apparent idleness; others
who could do best by walking alone in the open air;
others, by stating to themselves the problems they wish to
solve, and then going about all manner of business, trust-
ing from experience to something they call unconscious
cerebration. Each man, I take it, must find his own
method; at different times each man may find different
methods the best."

Graham Wallas cautioned against false relaxation that
can come from surrendering our own thinking processes
to those of someone else. Said he:

"Perhaps the most dangerous substitute for bodily and
mental relaxation during the stage of incubation is neither
violent exercise nor routine administration, but the habit

of industrious passive reading. Schopenhauer wrote that 'to put away one's own original thoughts in order to take up a book is the sin against the Holy Ghost.' During the century from 1760 to 1860, many of the best brains in England were prevented from acting with full efficiency by the way in which Greek and Latin classics were then read."

The processes of original thinking are the same wherever they may be employed and whatever may be their purposes. James W. Young, in his *A Technique for Producing Ideas,* applies the foregoing considerations to the creating of advertising copy. He outlines the process as consisting of the same three steps: accumulation, digestion or incubation, and finally, inspiration or synthesis.

Obviously, a clear understanding of this matter is of the utmost importance to every research worker and to everyone concerned in any way directly or indirectly with effective thinking and creativity. As the minimum essentials, the researcher must be provided with: (1) facilities for accumulating facts and experiences by reading, by personal contact, and by experiment; (2) opportunity to digest and collate these facts under circumstances conducive to the optimum exercise of his mental powers and favorable to inspiration or synthesis from them; and (3) the necessary means to prove and elaborate the results of these supreme mental processes.

While it is possible to achieve tremendous feats of imagination under quite deplorable conditions, modern industry cannot risk the uncertainty of such miracles. Rather, it must create and maintain the favorable conditions for research that invite inspiration. Even then, industry frequently becomes impatient when developments of world-shaking consequence cannot be delivered every hour on the hour. Although it is difficult to persuade research men to admit such a thing, it is also possible to provide too much ease and too great convenience for the researcher. In the extreme case, the process of relaxation and incubation may become so pleasant that the time of the researchers may be so wholeheartedly devoted to this phase of the operation (with neglect of the cognate activities of experiment and proof) that nothing at all is accomplished. One great research laboratory is said to approach this condition so closely that its inmates commonly speak of it as the "plush-lined rut."

Obviously here, as in every other phase of research, common sense must govern. Relaxation must be limited before it leads to mental flabbiness, and rigorous austerity must equally be avoided, lest it lead to mental sterility. Research, as all things, profits most from following a reasonable and happy medium between the two.

Let's see next how the methods we have discussed are employed profitably by examining some problems solved by them in industry.

CHAPTER 7

We Tackle Industrial Problems

Now that we have examined some of the various processes by which people think creative thoughts, solve problems of a great many kinds, and otherwise utilize their brains creatively, let's look into some specific applications of these principles. Industrial research *must* be productive, and so we'll look at that. We have already suggested the pattern that seems most satisfactory and the one most nearly universal with successful research workers, whether in industry or not. Of course, this pattern is modified in one detail or another by individual workers to fit their customary thought processes and to adapt the general method to individual problems. Here are the steps of some of these modifications.

Our basic pattern, which fits creativity in poetry, music, art, and every other field, including science, is some modification of this one:

(1) Recognize the problem and state it clearly.

(2) Accumulate and correlate data bearing on it.

(3) Digest the data and seek order and logic in it.

(4) Achieve a pattern that fits the facts and apparently solves the problem.

(5) Finally submit the solution to the test of trial.

Graham Wallas sets what is virtually the same pattern with four potent words. From his point of view, the creative process consists of these four parts: (1) Preparation; (2) Incubation; (3) Illumination, the flash of the arrival of the happy idea; and finally (4) Verification.

A common problem of industrial research is to develop a new process for the manufacture of some known compound or product. A procedure that has successfully solved even widely different problems of this kind reveals that the steps taken are almost identical, regardless of the nature of the process. These are the steps in order:

(1) Determine the need and state the broad problem.

(2) Review experience and the literature thoroughly.

(3) Select the seemingly best method to be examined in detail, the one holding the most promise.

(4) List all factors involved in this particular reaction or series of reactions. Include not only temperature, pressure, and concentration of individual elements, but also the physical and chemical properties of each substance that enters the reaction and the possible effects of catalysts and impurities.

(5) List the obvious methods of varying each factor. Note that what is obvious to one investigator may not be obvious to another.

(6) Select one or more factors to be varied successively, one at a time, with all others held constant.

(7) Vary these factors following methods based on studied familiarity with the technical facts.

(8) Experiment, and collect and study the resulting data.

The first factor selected to be varied and the first means of varying this factor may not solve the problem. Commonly, several methods of varying the selected factor must be tried and other, even secondary, factors need to be varied before you attain ultimate success.

A somewhat similar, but more detailed, series of steps was stated by the late William A. Hamor, assistant director of Mellon Institute of Industrial Research. Dr. Hamor suggested that the researcher: get the history of the problem; survey the literature; define the problem; study the attack; suggest solutions; determine needed data; select methods; outline the program; begin experiments; test solvability; verify findings; collect data; systematize data; analyze data; appraise results; make deductions; reach conclusions; test conclusions; and finally, plan development from the research.

While these several steps or others like them are vital to the solution, another phase must not be neglected. At more or less frequent and (most important) regular intervals, the researcher should draw up reports covering work done and conclusions that may be drawn from it. The report should summarize the latest experiments, literature readings, and just plain thinking on the problem. It must formulate the best statement of what the problem has become in the light of latest experience. This becomes the next question that the research must answer. The progress of the search is a consecutive series of statements of just what the problem has come to be. While it is usually necessary for the researcher to inform his colleagues, his superiors, or his backers of progress for reasons of business or policy, it is vital to his own efficiency that he draw up frequent reports to *himself,* if not to others.

The usefulness of this general plan of attack on a research problem can be best appreciated by considering examples. Langmuir repeatedly proved himself a master of the art of selecting just the right property or condition to be varied and then of getting the greatest possible good from his experiments. Undoubtedly, the extraordinary quality of his mind had much to do with this facility, but this faculty quite clearly shows itself in his penetrating and painstaking analysis of the problem before him at the beginning of the research. Obviously he did not content himself with varying one condition solely because it was easy, when another, more difficult to handle, might lead to quicker and surer conclusions. He suggested one of his valuable methods when he told about investigating the effect of extreme vacuum in incandescent lamps:

"It was the universal opinion among the lamp engineers with whom I came in contact that if only a much better vacuum could be produced in a lamp, a better lamp would result. Doctor Whitney (founder-director of GE research), particularly, believed that every effort should be made to improve the vacuum, for all laboratory experience seemed to indicate that this was the hopeful line of attack on the problem of a better lamp. However, I really didn't know how to produce a better vacuum, and instead proposed to study the bad effects of gases by putting gases in the lamp. I hoped that in this way I would become so familiar with these effects of gas that I could extrapolate to zero gas pressure, and thus predict, without really trying it, how good the lamp would be if we could produce a perfect vacuum.

"This principle of research I have found extremely useful on many occasions. When it is suspected that some useful result is to be obtained by avoiding certain undesired factors, but it is found that these factors are very difficult to avoid, then it is a good plan to increase deliberately each of these factors in turn so as to exaggerate their bad effects, and thus become so familiar with them that one can determine whether it is really worth-while avoiding them. For example, if you have in lamps a vacuum as good as you know how to produce, but suspect that the lamps would be better if you had a vacuum, say, 100 times as good, it may be the best policy, instead of attempting to devise methods of improving this vacuum, to spoil the vacuum deliberately in known ways, and you may then find that no improvement in vacuum is needed or just how much better the vacuum needs to be."

When, back in the days before World War I, I betook myself to the University of North Carolina to study chemistry, the first research that I encountered was the development of the cup-and-gutter system of gathering gum turpentine by Charles Holmes Herty. Dr. Herty, at that time head of the Department of Chemistry and idol of the whole student body, was fond of telling us of his department about the origins of the Herty cup, then widely employed throughout the pine belt of the South Atlantic and Gulf states. Herty had looked into the naval stores industry (producing valuable products from pine) when he was on the staff of the U. S. Forestry Service and had found the current methods of turpentine orcharding deplorably inefficient and wasteful. The method then employed had involved cutting a deep well, called a "box," into the base of the tree to catch the gum turpentine dripping into it from scars cut into the cambium layer beneath the bark of the tree. As the gum flowed sluggishly down the blazed surface, much of the valuable turpentine evaporated out of it, so that the yield of this constituent diminished as successive scarifications increased the distance the gum had to flow from the fresh cut to the box at ground level. Furthermore, the accumulated gum on the blaze and in the box was a distinct fire hazard, and the tree was weakened against storm winds by the deep-cut box penetrating part of its root system. Herty learned that the resin ducts where the resin is formed come into being only when the tree is wounded and in need of this healing balsam. That reinforced his idea that an efficient system of collection could be devised using a cup and gutters that would be moved up the tree as the chipping proceeded upward.

Three problems arose in connection with Herty's system. He planned to use a cheap earthenware cup hanging on a nail driven into the tree and galvanized iron gutters to lead the gum into the cups. But the lumber people, who would ultimately saw up the tree, objected to an ordinary iron nail that would injure their saws. So Herty found a zinc nail that could be sawed through with no harm. Then it developed that the largest cup that could be made on flower pot machines would overflow between the every-other-week visits of the gum gatherers, thus losing some of the exuded gum. This was a serious setback to the project because the next larger size pot had to be molded by hand instead of by machine and this ran the cost up beyond what seemed reasonable. One of Herty's favorite stories was how he finally made the larger pots by machine. The problem arose because the rotating male member of the mold would tear the soft plastic clay as the prospective pot or cup was taken out of the female stationary member.

With small pots this did not happen, but as soon as potters tried to mold larger pots on the machines, they always tore. Counter to the advice of experienced people in the ceramic industry, Herty went to what must have been great expense in those days to have a larger set of molds made, only to find his crepe-hanging advisors right—the larger pots tore apart coming out of the mold!

Broke, tired, and very much discouraged, Herty was on the point of giving up when the thought occurred to him that if he could prevent the soft clay from slipping while the rotating mandrel was withdrawn, then it might be possible for the plunger to push the molded pot out of the female mold without breakage. The more he thought of it, the more it seemed to him that this was the answer he sought. It would be necessary only to score the mold! But the potters would have none of it! Score that beautiful expensive mold? Never! And that seemed to be that. But the young man's faith wouldn't let the matter drop! So young Herty quietly gathered together a number of files from the toolroom and with them stealthily invaded the molding shed after everyone else had gone home for the night! What a chance! Every cent he had or could readily borrow was tied up in that mold, and here he was deliberately filing grooves in its wonderfully smooth, polished surface! But now the deed was done and no retreat was possible! In spite of the uproar among the potters next morning—and it was truly an uproar—Herty finally persuaded them to try his multilated mold. It worked! For the very first time, a molding machine turned out large pot after large pot, each perfect, and none of them broke when the rotating mandrel was withdrawn! These larger pots, the largest molded by machine up to that time, could catch the normal flow from each fresh chipped surface of the blaze on a pine tree and hold all of it until the gatherers could come for it. And that was the key to the success of the whole project.

Later, in the turpentine orchards where clay pots were

nailed to scarred surfaces of pine trees with zinc nails, a
new problem arose: the metal gutters seemed unable to
stay in place under the blaze, but dropped out after only a
day or two. That left the exuded gum no proper channel
to flow into the pot and as a result the expected saving
by the new technique was wasted on the ground. The story
of how this dilemma was solved was one Dr. Herty especially delighted in telling me, since I had come to the university from Bradentown, Florida, very close to the
Tallevast turpentine operation where the solution was
found. The gutters were simple strips of galvanized iron
bent longitudinally at an angle. These metal strips were
inserted into cuts made in the blaze surface with a broad
axe. Now, a broad axe has one flat surface and the
edge is ground on the other surface. It seems to have occurred to no one that the way the axe was held to make
the cut would make any difference, but one of the axe-
men on Herty's force happened to be left-handed and so
when he made his broad-axe cut in the face of the blaze
he stood on the opposite side of the tree from his right-
handed counterpart. No one noticed the difference, but,
strangely, all the gutters put in that day stayed in place
and did not fall out as others had habitually done. Finally
the cause was located in the way the cut was made! Stand-
ing on the left side of the blaze, the right-handed axeman
had held the axe with the flat surface up and the inclined
surface down. The left-handed axeman stood on the right
side of the blaze and when he made his horizontal cut,
the flat face of the axe blade was down. The difference
in the two cuts is that the flat surface does not distort
the wood fibers that are strongly compressed by the inclined face. Thus the woody fibers below the cut by the
right-handed axeman were compressed and distorted, allowing the gutter to drop out, whereas the left-handed
axeman's cut compressed the fibers on the upper side of
the cut and not those below. Obviously the distorted fibers,
weakened by the distortion, would let the gutter drop off

when it was above the weakened fibers; but, if the surface below the gutter was flat, the tendency of the distorted
upper fibers to return to normal would hold the gutter
more firmly against the strong undersurface! Thus the success of the project—and it had significant impact on the
economy of the naval stores industry in the decades before
synthetic solvents invaded turpentine's markets—depended
for its success on the solution of three unexpected subsidiary problems after the principal one of the production
of gum had been solved.

Perhaps this series does not seem to fit exactly with our
scheme of research outlined above, but actually, each new
idea was the result of studied and concentrated accumulation of facts and the digestion of these facts, until finally
the whole erupted in what may be called a lightning stroke
of inspiration.

Fitting more exactly to the pattern we have set up above
was one of my own experiences during our efforts to develop solid carbon dioxide (Dry Ice) as a commercial
and domestic refrigerant. The key facts were that solid
carbon dioxide evaporates at atmospheric pressure to a gas
without passing through a liquid phase and it does this
at a temperature of approximately $-78.5°C$. The heat
absorbed by a pound of carbon dioxide in passing from
solid to gas at $0°C$. is approximately twice that absorbed
by a pount of ice in melting. (Please note that we are thinking about a period when Thomas Midgley had not yet
revolutionized refrigeration in small units by his discovery
of the fluorinated refrigerants [the Freons]. At that time,
our competition was with ice, rather than with the now
universal small mechanical refrigerating units.)

Our problem was to use the cooling capacity of solid
carbon dioxide efficiently at a temperature far above that
of the refrigerant itself. We thought to do this by putting
more or less insulation between the cooled space and the
refrigerant in order to control the flow of heat to the latter,
and hence prevent wasteful supercooling of the space.

Thomas B. Slate (U. S. Patents 1,592,992, 1,595,426, and 1,634,089) had succeeded in making solid carbon dioxide a useful refrigerant by simply reversing the usual refrigerating practice of the time: instead of surrounding the product to be kept cool with the refrigerant as was common practice with ice, Slate reversed the system and surrounded the refrigerant with the product, enclosing the whole in an insulating container, efficient because water-free. This is effective if the product is unharmed by super-cooling far below freezing. But this failed utterly when the product to be kept cold was sensitive to freezing, as are many, even most, of those the housewife puts in her re-frigerator. Our small research staff had been concentrating on this problem for many months, for the market for our refrigerant would be tremendously expanded if we could come up with a satisfactory refrigerator car or a domestic refrigerator. Each of us was literally saturated with the problem of controlling heat flow from the cooled space to our solid carbon dioxide. "Wrap the block of refrigerant in paper, as many layers as necessary," concluded one man. This worked all right so long as the size of the block was substantially unchanged, but, as evaporation and shrinkage proceeded, the rate of heat absorption dropped and there was no way any of us could think of to take off one or more layers of paper automatically.

That was about the situation and our thinking on the day that our spirits were especially low and I said to my right-hand man, Howard McIlvaine, "Let's get out of here and get a real lunch for a change. I'm tired of this place and the pigeons will be thankful for our sandwiches!" We got out of our laboratory coats and spruced up to go out on the street. That alone did us both good and we re-laxed measurably when the German waiter brought us *Hasenpfeffer mit Kartoffelklösse und Bier*. About the time the *gemütlich* surroundings and the digestive process had soothed us from the irritation of failures, lightning struck! Or so it seemed! Only fluids, and not solids, could be auto-

matically moved in or out from around our solid refrigerant. Gases are notably poor conductors of heat but liquids
are substantially better. The ratio in thin layers is something like one to ten. Why not put our refrigerant in a
double-walled vessel and arrange it so that when the temperature around it went up, the gas (or vapor) in the space
would be pushed out by a liquid that would make contact
between the two walls of the vessel? Why not indeed! I
had no sooner explained my "stroke of genius" to Howard
than he was drawing diagrams on the tablecloth showing
how the thing could work. Before he had his drawing finished we left on the run for the lab to get to work on trying
it out. I still don't know how we got out of the restaurant,
nor how I paid the tab. All that is clear is that I hadn't a
cent in my pocket when I stopped at the grocer's on the
way home for some things my bride asked me to get, and
that the idea worked (U. S. Patents 1,870,684 and
1,887,687). We were working with ten-inch cubes of solid
carbon dioxide weighing 50 pounds, and the problem was
to hold the temperature constant as the blocks evaporated.
Our gas-liquid control of the heat transfer rate kept the
refrigerated space in our test boxes constant within about
one degree centigrade throughout the week it took for
our blocks to shrink from fifty pounds down to a few
ounces! Later we worked out the idea of controlling the
flow of carbon dioxide gas past the cold surface of the
refrigerant container as a means of controlling temperature
in the refrigerated space (U. S. Patent 1,883,939), and
that proved to be more practical for such applications as
refrigerator cars and trucks. This was another application
for the notion, the "stroke of genius," of the German restaurant, since we had been previously using flow of gaseous
carbon dioxide for the double purpose of transferring heat
and insulating the container (U. S. Patent 1,825,073 and
others).

The stories of Thomas Midgley Jr.'s two famous researches—that led to tetraethyl lead for controlling the

knock in gasoline engines and to the fluorinated hydro-carbons as safe refrigerants—have been so often repeated in Midgley's own words that we shall merely summarize them here. Working in the laboratories of the General Motors Company, Midgley sought a way to overcome the knocking tendency of gasoline engines that prevented raising the pressure of the explosion that theoretically should have increased their efficiency and hence power output. Instead of raising efficiency, higher compression in the engine reduced it substantially. Here was certainly Socrates' "thorn in the mind," and General Motors was irritated to the point of doing something about it. Charles F. Kettering, then head of GM research, assigned the task to Midgley but could give him only the sketchiest leads to start him off. Actually, here was a property of engines and of fuels that had apparently attracted no serious attention before and Midgley had no guidelines to follow, only the indication of thermodynamic theory that the higher the pressure in the cylinder at the start of the explosion, the higher the efficiency. In the true Edisonian manner, he tried everything he could think of, and only after many hundreds of experiments over several years did a theory emerge from his results. This was that knock, the power-wasting detonation of the cylinder charge, could be controlled and pressures raised profitably if a heavy metal could be carried with the vaporizing gasoline into the explosion zone. Lead, as the heaviest of the common metals, proved best and this could be introduced with the fuel into the explosion zone in the form of tetraethyl lead, a compound at that time utterly strange and practically unknown. There were still subsidiary problems before the new kind of fuel was everywhere available: the method of making the additive had to be worked out, as did methods of handling it and compounding it into the fuel; ethylene dibromide had to be made in hitherto unimagined quantities and introduced into the fuel to minimize fouling of spark plugs; and a thousand other minor problems had to be solved. But these could be defined and solved, processes unlike the groping in the dark that finally led to tetraethyl lead itself.

Where Midgley's fuel problem consumed years and entailed hundreds, if not thousands, of experiments before he could even define it, his second important search—for a nonflammable, nontoxic refrigerant—required hours for its solution and, after that, only the experiments necessary to confirm his conclusions. After he had been asked to investigate refrigerants for the Frigidaire division of GM, he found that all the refrigerants then in use (this was in the late 1920s) were composed of elements in one part of his periodic table. That pointed toward fluorine as essential to his solution, but everyone had been afraid of fluorine compounds because of the toxic and disagreeable properties of hydrofluoric acid, which resulted from hydrolysis of common fluorine compounds. But, said Midgley, it must form stable compounds that are nontoxic as well as nonflammable. When he and his associates produced a fluorine carbon compound, dichloromonofluoro methane, it proved his point: it was neither flammable nor toxic! It was the ideal refrigerant, and beyond that, it opened a whole new field of fluoro-carbon compounds that might very well be useful in meeting a variety of refrigerant needs. Total time: hours, not years.

The contrast between these two examples of the two ways a research may be planned and carried out is detailed in Midgley's Perkin Medal address in 1937 (*Industrial & Engineering Chemistry,* Vol. 29, page 241 [1937]). In the search for the key to knocking and high-compression gasoline engines, no one knew what to seek in the beginning and consequently the only way to get ahead with the problem was the method of many, many experiments, the Baconian method made famous by Edison. In contrast, the search for a safe refrigerant was practically pinpointed in the beginning and this gave the searchers a clear theory to follow, in the style of Aristotle of old and Bancroft in modern times.

The results of these two researches were fundamental revolutions in two industries; their effects reached into far-extending ramifications of both engines and refrigeration—and far beyond these two. Tetraethyl lead and the knock-free fuel it made possible set off revolutions in internal combustion engines for automobiles, trucks, tractors, and airplanes and similarly touched off a new trend of development in petroleum and fuels.

Safe, effective fluorocarbons primarily affected the refrigeration industry, but through this they profoundly affected the food industry, the domestic economy of our homes, and the development of frozen foods, and latterly were basic to the development of the multitudinous spray bombs that lend new convenience to operations as diverse as whipping cream, shaving, distributing pesticides, and painting.

Basic differences are well recognized between the pure science and academic research of the universities, and the specific applied science and research of the industrial company's laboratory. But between these extremes lie many intermediate kinds of science and research. These progress by almost imperceptible stages from completely untrammeled pursuit of intellectual goals to investigations vital to the economic life or death of a company. We can differentiate "pure" or "basic" research from its counterpart, industrial "applied" research, on the basis of the desired goal. If the objective is utility or economic gain, then we can class that research as "applied," in contrast to the pure research of the university that seeks no direct profit. No reasonable distinction between the two can be based on the research methods or the science involved.

Thus an academic research might study the sizes of particles in a series of emulsions. Experiments might be planned to determine the curvature of the globules associated with several pure emulsifiers or the amounts of each sorbed on the surfaces of the globules. The key word there is "pure" because, to be valuable as academic, or pure, research, the work must use only pure substances as emulsifiers.

A similar industrial research might be practically the same study of a series of emulsions prepared as commercial products. The difference would lie in the interpretation. In the pure research, instability of the emulsion might be necessary to obtain the desired data; but the objective of the commercial research would be a completely stable emulsion. In the pure research, only a pure emulsifier could be appropriate; whereas, in the commercial research, a pure emulsifier would give way to an efficient one, commercially obtainable at a relatively low cost.

The methods of investigation in the two might be identical: electrophoresis, rate of creaming, particle size by photographic measurement, and like techniques.

Another problem might be concerned with the effectiveness of an emulsion as a means to administer doses of a medicine or a vitamin. The practical problem would be solved when the essential dose could be given harmlessly—perhaps a matter of weeks. But an academic research would go far beyond to study emulsions, emulsifiers, and the mechanics or physiology of assimilation—a lifetime study.

Delay in finding an answer can often be more costly than years of research. A baby oil manufacturer used olive oil as his base. Unfortunately, although the olive oil remained pure in the sealed container, as soon as a bottle was opened, the oil developed rancidity. Rancid-smelling babies pleased neither mothers nor the manufacturer, and this seriously threatened good will. The problem was solved by adding an 'oxygen scavenger' (an antioxidant of the family widely used in fatty food products and chosen for its harmlessness) to protect the olive oil. The oxygen-scavenging agent selected did not affect the end product.

And the added cost was less than one tenth of a cent per pint.

Time was an essential factor in this result. Clearly this manufacturer had no interest in knowing more about the problem once he knew how to protect his product—and the babies. But that would naturally have been only the beginning of an academic research!

Most important is the "focus" of the investigation. This grows out of the background the investigator must bring to each problem, based on his accumulated experience. He must select attainable objectives and direct or "focus" his attention on these to the exclusion of side excursions that are unlikely to be immediately fruitful. To carry the idea of focus farther, the researcher must be able to decide where to point his lens and, at the same time, what lens —normal, wide-angle, or telephoto—to employ under each set of conditions.

Obviously, any research undertaken for industry must be planned with economy clearly in mind. Only with full understanding of the need can scientific work be designed and conducted to yield the greatest good to its sponsors. This is equally true whether the problem involves only a single test or analysis to meet an immediate requirement, or whether the matter grows into a continuing application of the newest of science to the broad problems of an industry and its products.

Without due consideration to the economic factors involved in both solving the problem and applying the solution, any research, test, analysis, or investigation may defeat its own purpose. It is futile, for instance, to learn of a new process if the raw materials consumed cost more than the probable value of the product. That is too elementary to need comment, but researchers turn up results of that kind with amazing frequency.

A case in point was a futile research into the recovery of germanium from coal ash. Germanium sold for $35 per pound and is present to the extent of a few hundredths of a percent in the ash of certain coals. Much time, effort, and money were spent in research on the recovery of this element newly important in our age of transistors but, when the results were translated into commercial recovery, it was found that the cost per pound of germanium by the new process was between $70 and more than $100 per pound. The source continues to be the zinc smelters.

Even if the question of economy does not enter, you can still encounter serious problems if you do not have pertinent experience to guide you, and if you don't understand all the conditions that affect the validity of tests made. Consider, for example, the luxury yacht *Sea Call*. Its story illustrates not only the dangers of electrolytic, or galvanic, corrosion, but it also warns against experimental work undertaken without due consideration of the underlying theory. Such experimentation too often leads to unsound and dangerous conclusions. The hull of the *Sea Call* was made of monel metal plates (67 per cent nickel; 29 per cent copper), with the exception of the stem, keel, sternpost, and rudder frame. These latter were made of steel for economy and to facilitate fabrication. Both monel and iron rivets were used.

After a few weeks in the water, many of the iron rivets failed. Holes had been eaten entirely through some of the steel parts which were three quarters of an inch thick. The vessel had to be condemned as unseaworthy and broken up without having made a single voyage, resulting in a loss of some half million dollars. Preliminary laboratory tests on plates of monel metal and steel connected together in sea water for several months had shown no excessive corrosion of the steel. However, this experiment had not taken into account the relatively enormous area of the cathode (monel metal) in comparison with the anode (steel), a half-million-dollar oversight based on failure to think out the whole problem first! In this case the enormously larger area of the cathodic monel metal in the ship's hull concentrated electrolytic destructive action on the comparatively tiny areas of the anodic steel members to corrode away the steel at a greatly accelerated rate, a factor neglected in the laboratory corrosion tests.

Scale deposits that form on the sea-water side of evaporators and other heaters long have annoyed marine engineers. The accumulation must be removed or the efficiency of the equipment is sacrificed. After several months' work, scientists devised a compound based on sulfamic acid that does a thorough cleaning job and is safe and easy to work with. Because the safety factor is high, cleaning can be done safely on shipboard by the crew, thus greatly reducing shipyard or other outside costs.

A paper manufacturer needed a method for preventing "brown-and-serve" rolls from sticking to the package. A chemist solved the problem with a new resin resistant to high temperature. A similar resin had been developed for a totally different application by the same laboratory and was ready at hand to solve the food packaging problem.

Then there was the case of the exploding marshmallows! The manufacturer faced near disaster when his packaged marshmallow product began popping like yeasty root beer while sitting quietly on dealers' shelves! Careful examination of both raw materials and finished product revealed the presence of a high bacterial count of anaerobes. These hardy little bacteria can withstand temperatures as high as those employed in making and sterilizing the product, and afterward produce carbon dioxide in large quantities, even without air and in tightly sealed containers. Once the cause was determined, the trouble was simply solved by more careful sterilization of ingredients going into the product.

CHAPTER 8

More Industrial Problems

Industrial research may be conveniently thought of in three great categories, depending on where the emphasis lies at the moment. The first category emphasizes the product; the second, the process; and the third, the equipment employed or to be employed. Each of these may be the nub of the question and, even in a single research, stress may move from one to another as the research proceeds. Nor is it always possible or desirable to assume that a hard-and-fast boundary can be erected between these several aspects of the greater problem of industry—production. Let us examine some typical cases fitting more or less neatly into these compartments.

New chemical products developed to meet existing needs have often proved highly profitable by providing the basis for entirely new industries. Ductile tungsten, rayon, cellophane, neoprene, Freon, nylon, and a host of others illustrate the point.

Methods in research of this type vary widely, since at the start there is no clear picture of the kind of compound or mixture sought. Sometimes investigators have no specific objective and no plan since they have not stated their problem clearly. The result may even develop as a by-product of another investigation. Often, the only idea is to extend the sales area of some product or products.

To develop a new chemical substance for a particular purpose, the method of attack may be based on the following steps:

(1) List the faults and the virtues of the present product.

(2) List similar products having properties that might be useful.

(3) Select a product having the fewest faults.

(4) Modify this product either fundamentally or by mixing with others to eliminate faults and enhance virtues.

Obviously, the steps involved are the same as in any other research, once the basic problem has been clearly stated.

John H. Long, manager of sales research for Hercules Powder Company during World War II, recognized three types of product research:

"First is a product and no market. Can it be used? Can it be offered at a profit by the seller with benefits to the prospective customer? Next is a market and no product. A customer wants something. Can it be developed from available raw materials, and be produced with facilities with which we are most familiar and which are available to us? Third is no product and no market, but an idea."

In the normal production processes, something may be left over—a waste, a by-product. The question arises: can this residue have value for somebody else or as something else?

A change in the process of extracting rosin, turpentine, and pine oil from stump wood left such a product after the recovery of the distillable terpene hydrocarbons and terpene alcohols. This residual resin was different from that obtained previously, a product without a market. The yield was substantial. For a short time, it was burned. Then it was stored in open bins. While study of the resin went on, the capacity of the storage bins was expanded time and again. Ultimately, that accumulated surplus resin, which at first appeared to be useless, became a regular article of commerce. It now serves needs of such diverse industries as paper and steel, asphalt and glass, phonograph records and Portland cement.

Next is a known market, but no product. That is quite different. Enterprising chemists always have been intrigued by the possibility of synthesizing the economically important constituents of natural essential oils, clearly a known market. The supply of oils is limited and the demand continuous.

For example, oil of anise and its commercially valuable derivative, anethole, are primarily imported from China. A dozen industries—toothpaste, dog food, bakeries, confectioners, perfumers—use anethole. Therefore, the possibility of making anethole from some basic material other than anise seed appeared to be decidedly worthwhile. Chemists know that anethole might be derived from terpenes by several methods.

"The first step, obviously, was to analyze the market," says Long, "and the next, to check potential supplies of raw material—adequate at reasonable prices, and not likely to be jeopardized except by cataclysm. Then, the patent situation was cleared.

"Then came the experimental work to test and to determine costs. With a larger-scale pilot plant, anethole was produced that duplicated the natural product and was soon being sold in worthwhile quantities."

The third category is little more than a question: if such and such could be made, would it be any good for this and that? Often, some chemist has thought of a novel chemical reaction or prepared a chemical with certain unique properties. It is only important if its properties are valuable and can be sold at a profit and to the benefit of the buyer.

"All sorts of variations are possible," Long tells us. "The customer wants to lower production costs. Or he wants to improve his product. The chemical he wants may never find its way into the end product—a frother in an ore flotation process, for example. Or it may be an important factor in controlling the physical properties of the end product—a stabilizer to maintain the initial clarity or color of plastics; or something to improve the durability of an automobile finish. Sometimes, the customer may have little knowledge of the chemistry of the new product he wants. Other times, he may have analyzed his problem so completely that he knows what chemical and physical properties are needed to give the performance characteristics he requires. He may even have made the chemical in his own laboratory but, for any one of a number of reasons, he may feel that you are the more logical producer."

Work of this type involves two variables, each of which can get easily out of hand: product development and market development. In the beginning, one of these must be set aside, and the exploration turned into the other.

The procedure followed at Hercules with its Resin 731 is a good example of this freezing and unfreezing of the market and product variables. It also is an example of a development which could not have succeeded without close liaison between research department and prospective customer.

Industry tackled the job of producing synthetic rubber in unprecedented volume during World War II and large quantities of soap were needed for the emulsion polymerization of the butadiene-styrene type of synthetic rubber. Soap derived from high-grade fat had been used but a suitable substitute would save a worthwhile quantity— some 100,000,000 pounds—of fats and oils. Rosin soaps had been used in a number of industrial processes, including emulsification, and these established products were tested against fatty-acid soap. A clean-cut market development.

A short-lived program showed that, while rosin soaps would emulsify butadiene and styrene, the yield of synthetic rubber was disappointingly low. No such reduction in the output of synthetic rubber could be tolerated; but polymerization plants, then under construction, were designed to operate under conditions that could not be met by the usual rosin soaps. But some rosin soaps performed less poorly than others. Polymerization was extremely sensitive to certain chemical types that inhibited reaction, and new inhibitors were being discovered every day. Because the supply of rosin was large and its price low relative to fatty acids, the exploration job got under way, studying a series of resin acids derived from rosin. Soaps from several of the resin acids gave a yield of polymer as high as the most active fatty-acid soaps. A market had been found. But the cost of producing several of the resin acids was exorbitant, others would require plant equipment unobtainable during the war, and another required an intermediate raw material not available in sufficient quantity. Eventually, a product was found and pilot plant production started on a resin that satisfied the requirements and solved the problem.

Typical of Long's second category, a market but nothing to satisfy it, is the development of the first synthetic plastic, Celluloid.

John Wesley Hyatt set out to win the $10,000 prize that had been posted in the late 1800s to reward the inventor of a satisfactory substitute for ivory billiard balls. Although the billiard balls that he made were of indifferent usefulness, the value of Celluloid, the synthetic plastic he developed, has been tremendous. Mr. Hyatt had this to say on the subject in his acceptance of the Perkin Medal for his many contributions to industrial science:

"My earliest experiments in nitrocellulose were incited by accidentally finding a dried bit of collodion the size and thickness of my thumb nail, and by my very earnest efforts to find a substitute for ivory billiard balls. From the first, it was apparent that a semi-liquid solution of nitrocellulose—three-fourths volatile liquid and yielding a final solid less than one-fourth the mass of the original mixture—was far from being adapted to the manufacture of solid articles; and that I must initially produce a solid solution by mechanical means. The only useful solvent known to me at that time was a mixture of alcohol and sulfuric ether; with the old formula (about equal parts of ether and alcohol) I mixed in a closed mill a thick paste of soluble cotton. After mixing, we removed the cover of the mill and evaporated the mass down to a thick dough. This we forced accurately around the ball (made of another substance), and allowed to dry. This resulted in a rather brittle coating, owing, as I found, to the unequal evaporation, leaving only the alcohol, a poor solvent by itself, at the final shrinkage. This was remedied by using only the least amount of alcohol (five parts ether to one alcohol) necessary as a solvent. Even this coating shrunk to less than half of its original thickness and required to be dried immersed in water under several hundred pounds' pressure per square inch to insure its solidity and freedom from bubbles. It became necessary to strain the mass by forcing it through a very fine sieve to exclude the unnitrated fibers. All these difficulties stood in the way of success, except in high-priced articles like billiard balls. Other seriously objectionable features became apparent. In order to secure strength and beauty, only coloring pigments were added, and in the least quantity; consequently a lighted cigar applied would at once result in a serious flame, and occasionally the violent contact of the balls would produce a mild explosion like a percussion guncap. We had a letter from a billiard saloon proprietor in Colorado, mentioning this fact and saying he did not care so much about it, but that instantly every man in the room pulled a gun.

"Finding in some patents that a little added camphor was beneficial, we conceived the idea of mechanically mixing solvents with the pulp and coloring matter while wet, then absorbing the moisture by blotting papers under pressure, and finally submitting the mass to heat and pressure.

"To our surprise, we noticed a slightly solvent action of the precipitated and washed camphor upon the pulp, even before the heat and pressure, and without other solvent we succeeded in producing a transparent slab onefourth of an inch thick, fine, and as hard as a piece of wood."

That was the first Celluloid. It was also the first synthetic plastic.

The problems of surpluses of products usually turn out to be process problems that require ways to be found to convert a drug on the market into a desired material. For example, after World War I, a producer of ethyl alcohol and acetone, both required in munitions manufacture, was left with excessive stocks on hand. Ethyl alcohol was particularly abundant. The acetone had been made from calcium acetate, which in turn was made from acetic acid produced by the fermentation of dilute ethyl alcohol.

The company not only had on hand large stocks of alcohol, acetic acid, and acetone, but it also had a large (and unfortunately idle) capacity for producing them all. Investigation of possible markets for these products in peace revealed, among other things, a possible demand for substantial quantities of ethyl acetate, which could be made from ethyl alcohol and acetic acid. It seemed logical, therefore, to seek a method of manufacturing ethyl acetate, useful as a solvent and otherwise, from the available raw materials, 95 per cent alcohol and dilute (10 per cent) acetic acid.

The literature disclosed the fact that to make ethyl acetate from alcohol and acetic acid it is necessary, or at least desirable, to have 100 per cent alcohol and 100 per cent acetic acid. These two compounds react in the presence of fairly high concentrations of a strong dehydrating agent, such as sulfuric acid. The yields, however, are rather low (around 60 per cent), probably because concentrated sulfuric acid destroys (oxidizes) these anhydrous organic compounds. Although sulfuric acid is a well-known dehydrating agent, it seemed possible that it might also be a catalyst. If so, lower concentrations could be effective. A series of experiments were first made to determine the most useful concentration of sulfuric acid. The hypothesis of catalytic action for the acid proved correct, since a concentration of sulfuric acid as low as 2 to 3 per cent brings the reaction in a mixture of 95 per cent alcohol and 10 per cent acetic acid to equilibrium in a comparatively short time. In other words, large quantities and high concentrations of sulfuric acid are not necessary.

This established the existence of a reasonably rapid reaction between 95 per cent alcohol and 10 per cent acetic acid in the presence of 3 per cent sulfuric acid to form ethyl acetate and water. The next factor worth investigating was the concentration of the two reactants. Quite obviously, anyone trained in physical chemistry would utilize the law of mass action by increasing the concentration of one or the other to force the reaction in the desired direction. Alcohol was chosen because it was simpler under existing conditions to increase its concentration than to raise that of acetic acid. A decrease in the concentration of one of the reaction products in the reacting zones should produce a similar effect. The research organization engaged on this problem was thoroughly familiar with the theories of distillation and fractionation and with the practical operation of fractionating columns. It was thought possible to decrease the concentration of products in the reaction by carrying it out in an ordinary fractionating column. Again the literature was searched, and an azeotropic mixture was found to be formed by the alcohol, ethyl acetate, and water. This ternary constant-boiling mixture has a boiling point lower than that of the familiar binary constant-boiling mixture of 96 per cent by volume of alcohol with 4 per cent by volume of water, and this in turn has a lower boiling point than any single component of the system. Therefore, if the reaction mixture is fed into the side of an ordinary fractionating column, a large proportion of the overhead product (that is, the more volatile constituent) consists of this ternary mixture and the column can be so regulated that only water and sulfuric acid leave it at the bottom. This possibility was tried experimentally and the results confirmed the surmise. Incidentally, an excess of alcohol introduced into the feed gave a product which showed no acetic acid. All of the acid had reacted; in other words, the yields were 100 per cent based on the acetic acid fed into the column.

At this point, a process had been devised operating at a satisfactory rate and giving 100 per cent yields on the basis of one of the constituents. The problem of converting the constituents at hand into pure ethyl acetate had been partly solved, and all that remained was to separate the products from the mixture in pure form. This also presented difficulties and required further research.

The azeotropic mixture contained all of the acetate formed and any attempt to separate it by simple fractional distillation would necessarily fail. The distillate would always be the original constant-boiling ternary mixture (consisting of 83 per cent ethyl acetate, 9 per cent alcohol, and 8 per cent water), and the residue would contain only the excess alcohol and water accidentally accompanying the azeotrope.

The problem of breaking down the azeotropic ternary mixture had to be solved before it was possible to concentrate the final product, ethyl acetate. From the literature, it was learned that in a mixture of three liquids one component usually acts as a blending agent for the other two. Addition of an excess of either liquid, not the blending agent, to such a ternary mixture reduces the concentration of the blending agent, and thereby separates the mixture into two liquid phases. In this particular case, one phase should contain a greater percentage of the ethyl acetate than the other. Experiment showed that adding water to the condensate from the top of the fractionating column caused a separation into two layers, the upper containing approximately 94 per cent ethyl acetate, 4 per cent water, and 2 per cent alcohol. The lower layer, consisting primarily of alcohol and water, contained a minor percentage of ethyl acetate. Incidentally, this lower layer was returned to the fractionating column onto a particular plate where the composition was approximately the same.

Thus the percentage of ethyl acetate was raised from 80 to 94 per cent. This was accomplished by operating with the concentration factor, and by using a well-known principle regarding the mutual solubilities of liquids.

In order to remove the final traces of alcohol and water from the mixture and thus to obtain practically 100 per cent ethyl acetate, it was only necessary to pass this mixture into another fractionating column. Ethyl acetate was in excess of the amount required to form the ternary mixture with the alcohol present. Consequently, from the top of the column came the constant-boiling ternary mixture (since it possessed the lowest boiling point of any constituent), and this was returned to the separator, where more water was added to repeat the process. At the bottom of this column appeared the finished product, approximately 100 per cent ethyl acetate. Once more, the factor of concentrations of the constituents had served and the well-known principle of fractional distillation was utilized to change these concentrations as desired.

In brief, this problem was solved by manipulation of the conditions of chemical and physical equilibrium by the application of common methods plus the utilization of specific knowledge regarding the physical and chemical behavior of the reactants. Note, too, how each successive step brought a new statement of the problem that narrowed it progressively.

Obviously, the key to this solution lay in the fact that sulfuric acid plays a catalytic, rather than a dehydrating, role in the reaction of ethyl alcohol with acetic acid. This had to be learned by experiments undertaken, in this case, because the raw materials available were expensive to concentrate and to dehydrate—steps that would have been necessary if the reaction would not proceed between them as they were. Distillation techniques were familiar to the organization faced with this problem and the necessary equipment was readily available. Furthermore, distillation as a method of changing concentrations of constituents already present in a mixture is preferred to salting-out or extraction methods, which introduce extraneous substances and increase the expense of the operation. The reasoning behind the steps suggested is readily apparent from the solubilities of the constituents in one another and the boiling points of mixtures.

This account of the way surplus alcohol and acetic acid were converted into salable ethyl acetate follows that by Donald B. Keyes, who participated in it. Now that a solution of the problem has been reached and the surpluses consumed, the method and the chemical and physical reactions involved have found important applications elsewhere. Developments in both the technology and the economics of the chemical industry have shifted many of the basic considerations behind this development; acetic acid now comes largely from natural gas and petroleum refinery gases and ethyl acetate is merely one of a number of useful solvents. But the research is still useful as a pattern for others.

After World War I, vast quantities of nitrocellulose, solvents, plasticizers, and diluents left from smokeless-powder production filled warehouses in this country. Our industrial plants housed equipment to produce these chemicals in enormous quantities. No market for them existed. The pigmented varnish of the day was extremely unsatisfactory for painting automobiles. A durable finish required many coats of a rather costly varnish to be applied and each given plenty of time to dry before the next was put on. The process took two weeks or so. This meant that the automobile industry must have in its plants two weeks' output of automobiles at all times undergoing the process of finishing. The cost in tied-up capital was terrific, quite aside from the expense of the process itself. Quite naturally, the automobile companies and the producers of nitrocellulose and solvents embarked upon researches on their apparently separate problems. Soon they got together and directed joint research toward producing a pigmented nitrocellulose lacquer which would dry rapidly and at the same time yield a durable finish. The great fault of older lacquers, not usable for automobile finishing, was the very high viscosity of the lacquer solution when it contained appreciable quantities of nitrocellulose. The development of the so-called low-viscosity nitrocellulose, yielding fluid instead of jelly-like solutions, and new and better solvents made possible modern lacquer and its utilization as an automobile finish. The time for finishing a car was reduced by the new lacquers from two weeks or more to a couple of hours. It is even related that Charles F. Kettering played a practical joke on a paint manufacturer by having his automobile completely refinished in a new color during a long luncheon!

Pigmented lacquer of the type first used had little or no brilliancy when applied to the automobile. An ingenious attempt to avoid this difficulty was the substitution of bright- and light-colored pigments for the carbon black and dark blue pigments inherited from the older varnish coatings. The surface was still dull, but it gave the casual observer an impression of gloss from its light and brilliant color. Eventually, the public demanded more gloss, and it was produced by a change in gum content and of the plasticizer in the lacquer.

Nitrocellulose lacquer, although a vast improvement over the older varnishes and enamels, was nevertheless too expensive to be wholly satisfactory. About 75 per cent of the lacquer was solvent, or a combination of solvents, whose sole function was to liquefy the nitrocellulose until it was applied and then evaporate from the surface as the lacquer dried. In other words, approximately 75 per cent of the material was thrown away, and the coating left on the automobile from considerable quantities of lacquer was very thin. Furthermore, evaporation of the solvent from the surface tended to form a skin over the surface which must be punctured for the solvent underneath to get out. The final film, especially an unpigmented one, was often full of holes which allowed water vapor and oxygen to pass readily through to corrode the metal below. Clearly, nitrocellulose lacquers were far from ideal.

Subsequent attempts succeeded in revolutionizing the finishing of automobiles again. The successful attack was based on the solution of synthetic resins in an unpolymerized state in drying oils in much the same way that natural resins (the copals) were dissolved in oil to yield varnishes. Bakelite, a condensation product of aldehyde and phenol, was studied early. Such a condensation product was incorporated with lacquer and a drying oil and the combination produced a finish quite as durable as lacquers but at the same time yielding a film considerably thicker, far more brilliant in appearance, and having a smooth, glossy surface. Subsequent developments have employed other resin-forming compounds.

The general method of process research applies equally well to chemical and physical processes. The physical process of producing anhydrous ethyl alcohol from the 96 per cent product, for example, involves no chemical reactions, but this problem can be readily solved by the method already illustrated. Constant-boiling ternary mixtures, readily formed by alcohol and water with a third substance, have water and alcohol contents in considerably different ratios from the 4:96 proportion of their binary constant-boiling mixture. All that is necessary is to feed into the side of a fractionating column a binary mixture of alcohol and water plus the quantity of the third substance to form a ternary azeotrope. Benzene is conveniently used. Out of the bottom of the column, when properly adjusted, will come 100 per cent alcohol, and from the top, a ternary mixture approaching the composition of the constant-boiling mixture of the three constituents.

As noted above, the alcohol and benzene in the constant-boiling mixture can be recovered by cutting down the percentage of the blending agent—in this case, alcohol—by adding an excess of one of the other constituents, for example, water. Two liquid phases appear; most of the benzene is in the upper layer and most of the alcohol and water in the lower.

Of course, the entire process can only be made efficient by recovering all of the alcohol and all of the benzene. This can be done by the standard procedure. The water layer containing most of the alcohol and a little of the benzene is fed to a second fractionating column. Off the top of this column comes the ternary constant-boiling mixture, which is returned to the separator. From the bottom comes the excess alcohol and water. This mixture, in turn, can be sent to a third fractionating column, yielding the constant-boiling binary mixture of alcohol and water, which can be sent back to the feed plate of the dehydrating column. From the bottom comes the excess water. The benzene layer can be sent to a fourth fractionating column, off the top of which will come the constant-boiling ternary mixture (as it has the lowest boiling point) to be returned to the separator. From the bottom of this column comes fairly pure benzene to be returned to the feed plate in the dehydrating column. We now have a process which uses as a raw material 96 per cent alcohol and gives as products anhydrous alcohol and water. The simplicity of this research lies in the fact that it is entirely physical in nature and it is unnecessary for the research worker to employ any method of changing the factor of concentration other than that previously discussed.

A much older research and its subsequent development still remains, in its significant parts, an important economic producer. Charles M. Hall's process for producing metallic aluminum marked the vital turning point in the technology of metallurgy and converted what had been a precious metal into an everyday convenience. The way in which Hall developed the method for the production of aluminum supplies an excellent example of the step-by-step approach. The story in Hall's own words was told by him in accepting the Perkin Medal in 1911. Here it is in part:

"I read about Deville's work in France, and found the statement that every clay bank was a mine of aluminum and that the metal was as costly as silver. I soon after began to think of processes for making aluminum cheaply. I remember my first experiment was to try to reduce aluminum from clay by means of carbon at a high temperature. I made a mixture of clay with carbon and ignited it in a mixture of charcoal with chlorate of potassium. It is needless to say that no aluminum was produced. I thought of cheapening the chloride of aluminum then used as the basis for aluminum manufacture, and tried to make it by heating chloride of calcium and chloride of magnesium with clay, following the analogy by which iron chloride is produced when common salt is thrown into a porcelain kiln. A little later, I worked with pure alumina and tried to find some catalytic agent which would make it possible to reduce alumina with carbon at a high temperature; I tried mixtures of alumina and carbon with barium salts, with cryolite, and with carbonate of soda, hoping to get a double reaction by which the final result would be aluminum. I remember buying some metallic sodium and trying to reduce cryolite but obtained very poor results. I made some aluminum sulfide but found it very unpromising as a source of aluminum then, as it has been ever since."

From today's point of view, it is necessary to remember the dates when Hall was working and to recall that much of the technology we take for granted had not yet been developed then. Even electricity from nearby power lines was still in the future in the 1880s, and electroplating was much more a scientific toy than a practical technique.

"On a later occasion," Hall continued, "I tried to electrolyze a solution of aluminum salt in water, but found nothing but a deposit of hydroxide on the negative electrode. I did not give a great deal of time to these experiments, as I was then a student in college and was working on three or four attempted inventions.

"I had studied something of thermochemistry, and gradually the idea formed itself in my mind that if I could get a solution of alumina in something which contained no water, and in a solvent which was chemically more stable than the alumina, this would probably give a bath from which aluminum could be obtained by electrolysis.

"In February, 1886, I began to experiment on this plan. The first thing in which I tried to dissolve alumina for electrolysis was fluorspar, but I found that its fusing point was too high. I next made some magnesium fluoride, but found this also to have a rather high fusing point. I then took some cryolite, and found that it melted easily and in the molten condition dissolved alumina in large proportions. I rigged up a little electric battery—mostly borrowed from my professor of chemistry, Professor Jewett of Oberlin College, where I had graduated the previous summer. I melted some cryolite in a clay crucible and dissolved alumina in it and passed an electric current through the molten mass for about two hours. When I poured out the melted mass I found no aluminum. It then occurred to me that the operation might be interfered with by impurities, principally silica, dissolved from the clay crucible. I next made a carbon crucible, enclosed it in a clay crucible, and repeated the experiment with better success. After passing the current for about two hours I poured out the material and found a number of small globules of aluminum. I was then quite sure that I had discovered the process that I was after.

"I undertook to broaden and improve the method, and found that I could use, instead of cryolite, other double fluorides, particularly a double fluoride of potassium and aluminum. The most important change, however, which I made at this time, was in the material used as an anode. I wanted to get rid of the burning up of the carbon anodes. I tried a platinum anode and found that it seemed to work all right, but it was too expensive. I discovered that if I used a fusible bath of a potassium double fluoride with a sodium double fluoride, I could use a copper anode, which immediately became coated with a thin film of copper oxide and acted like a permanent platinum anode. This was not a step in advance as I had hoped, because more or less copper got into the reduced aluminum, and the use of a copper anode led me to use very fusible baths, which on the whole did not work as well as the less fusible baths. It is probable that this change delayed a successful result for a year or two.

"When worked on a small scale, this process with any of the baths I have mentioned, and with either copper or carbon anodes, is not apparently promising. The ampere efficiency is low, sometimes zero, and the bath, whether composed of sodium or potassium salt, becomes filled with a black substance which accumulates and renders the process very difficult. I presume that my friend, Dr. Heroult, who invented the process independently in France about the same time, encountered the same difficulties. In spite of the difficulties mentioned, however, I had great faith in the theoretical possibilities of the process, and believed that the practical obstacles could be overcome, so I stuck to it from the start.

"In December, 1886, I returned to my home in Oberlin, continued my study, and found that a bath composed of a very fusible double fluoride of aluminum and potassium, with copper anodes, worked much better than anything I had before tried. I have a number of buttons of aluminum made by this method at that time. The larger one was made with current from a galvanic battery on December 7, 1886, and weighs about 8 grams."

From this point, Hall, like most inventors, became much involved in efforts to obtain backing for his idea. This was a rocky road for Hall, as it is for most independent workers, in spite of the fact that his method developed into an industry that has made aluminum both common and cheap, a remarkable achievement when you consider that he started at a time when aluminum metal was more costly than gold and much rarer!

Perhaps the most productive type of product research is based on suggestion. A new compound never made before, or made only for a specific purpose in very small amounts, has unique properties and is produced on a generous pilot-plant scale. Sometimes a new process is employed. Liberal samples are distributed among research organizations who might be interested. Its physical and chemical properties are well publicized in articles and advertising. In the course of time, someone working in another organization is almost sure to find a real use for the new product to meet a particularly urgent need. A case in point is the development by the petroleum industry of furfural as a selective solvent for refining lubricants, a use never suspected by the producers of furfural.

However, if the problem is to produce a new substance for a specific purpose, the original method of attack outlined above is the only feasible one. Success or failure largely depends on the second step: listing all possible substitutes for the old compound or mixture. Experience has shown that the broader the view in preparing this list, the more likely is success.

In seeking a substitute for tincture of iodine as an antiseptic, one group of investigators suggested the mixture, used in analytical chemistry, of potassium iodide, potassium iodate, and an acid salt (the one finally selected was anhydrous aluminum sulfate). When dissolved in water, this particular mixture reacts to liberate free iodine. This particular dry mixture could be formed into tablets which would yield an antiseptic solution when placed in water. The faults of the tincture of iodine were recognized as: first, a usual excess concentration of iodine tends to burn the flesh and do more harm than good; and, second, the alcohol used as a solvent irritates the wound. The iodine content of the new mixture could be controlled, and this control, with the absence of alcohol, should make it an effective and practical antiseptic. This proved to be the case.

Somewhat different schemes are characteristic of the creative thinking of those who seek to adapt equipment of one kind or another to a variety of purposes. Analogy is a potent part of much creative thinking, but in this relatively restricted area of specialized equipment, analogy is both the most useful and at the same time the most common theme. John V. N. Dorr, whom we met briefly in Edison's laboratory earlier, supplied us with clear-cut examples of the value of analogy in development of an idea. Dorr left Edison to go to the gold fields of South Dakota in the final years of the nineteenth century. Here he encountered a number of processes employed in the recovery of gold that seemed to him to need attention—his or someone's like him. The cyanide process was in its early stages, and by utilizing the solvent effect of cyanide solutions on gold in the finely ground ore, this new process offered promise of recovering important values from the discard piles of miners who had depended on less efficient older methods of recovery. Furthermore, the cyanide process raised the amount of gold that could be got from virgin ore. Dorr first addressed himself to the problem of separating and concentrating very finely divided slime from a suspension and doing this by a continuous method instead of the batch method previously used.

In Dorr's continuous classifier, the wet pulp from a suitable crusher or pulverizer is continuously conveyed to a settling trough. Here the sands settle to the bottom by gravity, while the slimes remain in suspension in the liquid. The slimes overflow into a launder that conveys them away from the classifier to a suitable container. At the same time, the sands are moved upward along the inclined bottom of the trough and delivered to another launder, which conveys them to the leachers. For moving the sands out of the trough, Dorr employed rakes, or scrapers, that move back and forth above the bottom of the trough. These rakes pull the sands toward the upper end of the trough on the upstroke, but they are elevated above the plane of the sand on the downstroke. This raking operation is effective in moving the sand toward the sand launder as fast as it settles. It also loosens or agitates the sand by forming it into small piles, allows these to settle between upward strokes, and progressively moves the sand upward and outward along the inclined bottom of the trough. The rakes effectively remove the sand, but move slowly so as not to agitate the liquid and interfere with the settling of the sand. The operation is regulated to keep the slime in suspension and allow the sand to settle out. When the sand is thus spread out in a thin layer, the liquid has a better chance to act upon it.

While most of the slime is separated from the sand in this way, some fine material still remains in the settled sand and must be removed. To accomplish this, Dorr provided means for washing the settled sand after it emerged from the settling bath and just before it is delivered to the launder that conveys it away. He put perforated pipes near the sand-delivery end of the trough and forced clear liquid through these and up through the sand. This eliminates the remaining slime and carries it back to the settling bath. The settled sand, in motion only half the time, is exposed to the flow of clear liquid from the perforated pipes, both in motion and at rest. This keeps the sand loose and open, and allows the escape of the slime. This classifier produced perfectly clean, leachable sand and left the slime entirely free from sand.

Like many another novelty, the ore classifier solved one problem only to reveal another. After you put the water suspension of your pulp through the classifier, you were faced with the problems of treating the separated sand— that was easy—and the suspended slime—that was not. You could simply run the slime suspension into tanks and let the solids settle out. But that was scarcely practical. The continuous overflow from the classifier accumulated too fast. Tanks and more tanks filled and overflowed with slime suspension waiting to settle. Then, when this problem of providing tanks to settle out slime became acute, Dorr made his second invention. Obviously, a continuous settling device must be the answer.

The problem was to provide a wide, relatively shallow vessel in which the relatively heavier suspended solids could settle out as the suspension progressed—from a feed launder at the center to an overflow flume around the circumference of the vessel, where the suspending liquid had become clear. The slime settled to the bottom as a thickening mud, just as it would do in a batch tank. But Dorr built into his device a series of scraping plows so mounted that they would move the slime slowly (to prevent stirring it up) toward an outflow in the center of the bottom of the settling vessel. At this point, the thin mud (or thick suspension) is pumped out by a diaphragm or other suitable pump. The important advantages of the system are that the amount of suspension, and hence of tank capacity, can be materially less than would be required by a batch process, and the sediment is removed while still in a thick liquid state that can be pumped, instead of the dense cake that often had to be dug out of the batch settling tanks.

These were Dorr's original inventions and in the three score years since their beginnings, analogy has shown the way to apply them in the most widely diverse situations. Recovery of magnesium from the extreme dilution of sea water, production of sugar from beets and from cane juice, beneficiating the greatest variety of ores (copper, iron, aluminum, titanium, and many others), treating water supplies and sewage, and numerous other operations have employed Dorr's equipment and the techniques of hydrometallurgy. These techniques seem to take on a variety of aspects and applications depending on the point of view of the person viewing them. So long as ores and the gold cyaniding process were uppermost in thinking about them, they belonged to metallurgy, but as soon as one could think of them as dealing with solids and liquids in relation to each other, the picture changed fundamentally. No metallurgy is involved in clarifying the water supply of Richmond, Virginia; nor in the purification of beet extract in Michigan. And certainly there is no metallurgy in taking the silt out of water flowing into irrigation canals in our Southwest or in caustic soda production in Savannah, Georgia. But all of these are basic problems of liquid-solid mixtures that must be separated. The analogy of other processes to sand and slime in the gold fields is seldom clear until one thinks of the process as treating liquid-solid mixtures.

Development of the specialized equipment of the chemical industry, as well as the adaptation of existing forms to new applications—what Dorr did—can be best accomplished in the semi-works or pilot plant. Here, the tools of chemical industry can be built at comparatively low cost in small sizes and modified cheaply as required by circumstances. Thus design and redesign of equipment is one of the several important functions that make the pilot plant a valuable adjunct of chemical research. That we shall consider next.

CHAPTER 9

We Progress to the Pilot Plant

Even the finest research, the most magnificent reasoning backed by the most convincing experiments, cannot achieve its full value until it is put to use. The idea in the researcher's mind, which is ultimately born in the research laboratory and passes its infancy there, only reaches manhood when it becomes the basis of a production process operated on a scale that lets all enjoy its benefits. That can be its whole history; like some people, it *can* pass from infancy to manhood directly. But that is not the best progression for an idea, any more than it is for a person. The transition from untrammeled infancy to manhood burdened with serious responsibilities is never easy, and the man is far better able to shoulder his proper share if this transition has been eased for him by an adolescent period of gradual learning about and approaching manhood. The same is true of the growing up of a research—a similar period of development of an idea is afforded by the pilot plant, an operation where the process, or equipment, or product, goes through a penetrating examination and development that ultimately fits it for the manhood of production.

Chemical industry's pilot plant guides its progress. Faced with serious difficulties in translating theoretical possibilities and laboratory experiments into going manufacture, the chemical industry invented the semi-works or pilot plant to "make your mistakes on a small scale so that your profits can be on a large one," as Leo H. Baekeland put it. Or, in the words of Kettering, the pilot plant is "a bridge across the shirt-losing gap" between laboratory experiment and plant production. The chemical industry had to develop something of the kind for its own survival, since only in the most remote case can chemical processes be economically enlarged from test tube to tank directly without serious trouble. Chemical reactions differ inherently from mechanical operations, which can be multiplied simply by installing more machines of the same kind. Two machines make twice as many cigarettes as one, but to attempt to jump from a bare chemical idea or experiment directly to full-scale production is to court almost certain failure from the misfunction of little things (and others not so little). The cost of interruptions, spoiled goods, and wasted time thus entailed can readily smother an otherwise promising development.

To avoid these casualties, which have plagued it whenever progress is rapid and development general, the chemical industry has devised and adopted the technique of the pilot plant, capable of small-scale operation under close control, as a means of exploring new territory. This valuable tool, now well developed, could be profitably adopted by other branches of industry to carry out their explorations and to promote their progress.

Chemical processing involves numerous factors not well understood and hence difficult to evaluate. Theory and the operations of the laboratory are, so far, unable with certainty to convert a bare idea directly into a going manufacture. When, in the exceptional case, this is attempted, the operation of the full-scale plant is subject to hazard from little failures that often cost many times the reasonable expense of the intermediate pilot plant step. The pilot plant eases the chemical industry through the transition from grams and ounces to pounds and tons and possesses other important values, as we shall see.

Operations in the pilot plant require careful planning so that they may cover successfully the interval between test tube and full-scale plant, and reasonably give the findings meaning. Not only is pilot plant equipment built of materials more like those in the production plant than laboratory glassware, but the increased scale of working introduces new and important differences. The basic fact

WE PROGRESS TO THE PILOT PLANT

is sometimes overlooked that the surface of a vessel, through which heat passes, increases as the square of the dimension, while the volume goes up as the cube of the dimension. That peculiarity of enlargement or shrinking sizes of units must always be uppermost in the mind of the pilot plant operator if he is to be successful. Clearly, doubling the dimensions of a tank raises its capacity eight-fold, but increases its surface (assuming its shape is the same) only fourfold. For one example, such an increase in size would raise the heat output of any chemical reaction involved by a factor of eight, but the surface through which this heat must be carried away would increase only four times. In other words, the surface of the large vessel would be inadequate—only half as great per unit of volume as the surface of the small one.

In a very real sense, the pilot plant is the halfway house of the chemical industry, for all the different phases of the industry meet here. Here the research chemist puts his reactions to their first test of production, but on a scale that avoids bankruptcy if they fail and undue danger if they run wild. Here the plant operating department, looking for improvements, can subject processes to the closest scrutiny by varying operating conditions without interrupting regular production. By operating processes in the pilot plant on a scale large enough to give meaning to the measurements taken from them, the engineering department can determine most, if not all, of the facts required to arrive at an efficient design for the full-scale production plant. Pilot plant operation can readily supply sufficient quantities of a new product, or of a new modification of an old one, for distribution by the sales department to prospective users. This can yield a dependable estimate of market possibilities—covering quality, quantity, and price of the product. All of these data, assembled and correlated, give management a penetrating analysis of the situation with which to form a firm base for its decisions.

The pilot plant can, when properly used, safeguard the

judgments of all concerned in the success of any enterprise. At the same time, it provides a reasonable and practical meeting ground, more logical than the usual conference room, for settling differences between departments and for forming policies for the future. Here every aspect of each problem can be studied with great care and here the interchange of ideas and points of view between the several groups constituting the company's staff can take place on the common ground of determined facts.

An instrument so potent for the good of an organization must of necessity be handled with skill and understanding if all its possibilities are to be realized. The pilot plant can yield abundantly if it is (1) amply equipped, (2) staffed by capable persons, and (3) well understood by all departments of the company. A genius might possibly be able to produce results from a pilot plant whose equipment is drawn entirely from the junk pile of the maintenance department's final discards. But a genius could get along without a pilot plant at all! Since pilot plants must be run by average to excellent research workers to give day-to-day good performance and not by geniuses to perform miracles, both the equipment and personnel of the pilot plant must be adequate.

Necessarily, the details of the pilot plant are determined by the general nature of its problems. The pilot plants of a glass works, a petroleum refinery, a textile mill, and a dyestuff plant are totally different from each other, except in their basic elements. For instance, each would need space enough to set up miniature duplicates of the principal units of equipment of the parent plant, and room beyond that to allow these units to be moved about into various combinations. Furthermore, each unit must be so situated that every part of it can be reached for measurements, alteration, cleaning, repair, and any other purpose that the operator may be able to imagine. The working space of the pilot plant must be heated and ventilated adequately for its purposes and must be provided with all the services of the plant itself: water, sewer, steam, electricity, fuel, gas, vacuum, air pressure, and any others available. Every reasonable, and some unreasonable, safety devices must be at hand. The equipment of the pilot plant must include as a minimum an adequate set of mechanical tools for setting up and dismantling any or all of its equipment and every type of measuring (and preferably automatically recording) device and instrument that may reasonably bear on its problems. Finally, some provision must be made for the assembly and recording of data, at least a desk in a separate room where records can be kept and calculations made.

Beyond these basic items, the pilot plant ordinarily duplicates the operating plant in miniature. Size is the most obvious difference but, in addition to that, the essential flexibility of the pilot plant requires a generous use of tees, unions, and flanged connections on each unit and plenty of thermometer wells and other connections for gages and meters of various kinds. Equipment should be mounted on dollies or casters to be easily moved about as needed. Large, heavy items—hydraulic presses, jacketed pressure vessels, furnaces, and other cumbersome major pieces—can be permanently mounted on solid foundations, depending for flexibility on bringing up lighter items to be connected into the various systems required. Mechanical industries can profitably set aside a single production line in the plant for pilot purposes, or build one specially.

The personnel of the pilot plant staff is even more important than its physical equipment. The prime necessity is to provide a skeleton staff of one or more persons to be permanent. This staff must be experienced in as many aspects of the company's business as possible, and certainly the director of the work must be thoroughly familiar with the points of view of research, production, sales, and management. His inclination to go off the deep end in a research sense must be tempered by his desire in an operating sense to produce results as fast as needed; his salesman's optimism must be mixed with a generous share of management's conservatism. This individual must be so independent of each of these several divisions that none of them dominates him and that his thinking is not incompatible with any of them. Obviously, such a person is impossible to find; but at least he is the one that should be sought, and the compromise person who is finally selected should be given a position as far as possible independent of each of his best customers—the company's department heads.

Having installed a minimum permanent staff in the well-equipped pilot plant, the next question is: how shall it function to best advantage? Necessarily, someone from each of the other departments of the company interested in a particular problem must be available to solve it for himself with any needed assistance from others. When the pilot plant research approaches a point where someone other than its originator should be interested and should prepare to take over, then an appropriate person from that department should be available on loan. No one whose primary interest is in some other department should become permanently attached to the pilot staff. It is equally wrong not to send men from other departments into the pilot plant at reasonable intervals, because each man can contribute to its effectiveness and each can learn something from it. M. C. Whitaker, chemical engineer, teacher, industrialist, once emphasized the difference in men about the plant thus: "A man who is essentially a plant man is likely to be a nuisance in a research laboratory; and on the other hand, a man with research inclinations is a hazard to any production process." Yet these two types of men can safely and effectively meet in the pilot plant. Here the research-minded man can experiment to his heart's content without interfering with the regular progress of raw material into the main production line, and of finished goods out of it to customers. The production man, for his part, can watch *in operation* equipment more substantial than the glassware of the laboratory; he can also see a certain orderly progress of affairs that can be influenced and adjusted with a wrench and a screwdriver instead of a glass blower's lamp and a piece of rubber tubing.

Here, too, the salesman can acquire some acquaintance with, and respect for, the processes and equipment that give him a product to sell. He can even operate the process himself without fear of drawing down the management's Jovian lightnings should something fail to go just right. This familiarity with his own product and a nodding acquaintance with the problems of others in supplying it have never yet been known to mar a salesman's effectiveness.

Finally, the pilot plant provides an effective initiation for any person entering a company with the expectation of assuming some responsibility for its affairs, either at once or later. The pilot plant's very nature makes this function simple and easy, as well as time-saving and effective. Visitors are always problems in an operating plant and neophytes who are not definitely training to become operators must be classed as visitors, whatever may be their histories and expectations. The operating force can seldom shut down an operation just to show a visitor how it works and certainly a shutdown cannot be timed to suit the visitor's whims. On the other hand, a trainee in the pilot plant can be given, under careful supervision, useful work to do in connection with its operation, and so earn his salt while learning.

No research and no development can be considered complete until it has survived the test of at least pilot plant operation. Here the research man continues to foster and cherish his offspring, but here he must transfer it by degrees to others' care. A process in the pilot plant may be considered to be in a period of adolescence. The research man has complete control of it in its infancy, but in the pilot plant his infant must go through a process of growing up, of passing from the secure dependence of the research laboratory to the hazardous maturity of operation. It undergoes tremendous enlargement, but, at the same time, the new process is acquiring a purpose only dimly imagined in the laboratory.

Normal routine would require that the research man (or one chosen from the group, if several have participated in the investigation) leave the laboratory and take his brainchild into the pilot plant. Here appropriate steps put the new process into operation. The staff of the pilot plant participates with the researcher in this and, as the work develops, representatives of the engineering department are called in to help things along. At a later stage, a designated person from the sales department and another from the operating department may be called in to contribute to the development. Naturally, the sales department has no particular interest in the development of a totally internal process which will not affect the products for sale. Nor will the production department show serious interest in a totally new product until the sales department reports some actual or potential interest in it from the company's customers. Thus the burden of proof continues to rest at the point of origin, the research department, until some probable value of the development has been demonstrated. All of this consumes considerable time, but it also makes important opportunities to study the new process, to determine its operating characteristics, and to make enough of the product to develop some interest in it from potential customers and others than its parents in the research laboratory. The bugs in the process revealed by engineering and production, and those in the product found by sales and customers, are gradually cleared out.

Obviously, blunders made in development are far less serious in their effects on the pilot plant scale than if they had happened in a production plant. But that in no way excuses the temporary or permanent members of the pilot plant staff if they simply blunder ahead thoughtlessly without a careful plan. Far too often the research man abandons his brains at the door of the pilot plant and, because he understands that it is the place to make mistakes, proceeds to make every reasonable error and some utterly unreasonable ones. The plant man and the engineer do the same thing, and the pilot plant operator is the victim of them all.

Troubles sometimes arise because the value and function of the pilot plant are not understood by outsiders or by those temporarily on its staff. Too often the pilot plant is thought of as being an extension of the other fellow's territory reaching out toward one's own, when actually it is an independent entity between the two, belonging to neither and to both.

Design of pilot plant processes which will function adequately is an important study in itself. Unfortunately, too little attention has been paid to it, presumably on the assumption that the good sense of all concerned will arrive at a reasonable and effective compromise and that such a compromise will be the thing desired. It may or may not be. The mere fact that it is a compromise does not guarantee its value. Furthermore, it is repeatedly evident that failure can happen quite as readily between laboratory and pilot plant as between that and the full-scale plant. And it is not impossible for a process to succeed in the full-scale plant when it has previously failed in both laboratory and pilot plant.

The basic problem of the pilot plant process thus is: to enlarge the laboratory experiments, to shrink the plant operation, and to give the intermediate stage some logical and evaluable relation to each. This is by no means easy, but when thoughtfully achieved it provides vital information on which all members of the policy-forming group of a company can base thoughtful decisions. The practice of the chemical industry certainly points the way for others to follow in the use of this invaluable tool of management and growth.

So we come to the point where we must interest others

in our idea, product, or process; and that requires records of all that has gone before, to supply a base for patents and publicity. This, too, is a vital part of the overall creative process, as we shall see in the next chapter.

CHAPTER 10

We Must Be Able to Tell Others

Your job of creativity is incomplete until you have put it to use. An unfinished bit dangles about, even after you have successfully taken all the steps we have suggested—charged your mental battery with facts, assimilated and organized these into a high-pressure charge, achieved the inspired flash of genius, and finally tested and proved your conclusions. Perhaps someone else can do much of this remaining chore for you, but you, and no one else, must report in substantial detail just what you have learned and what you think should be done about it. After that report is completed, the project must be evaluated from the several points of view and, finally, the novel part of your conclusions must in the great majority of cases be claimed as yours either by applying for a patent (or copyright) or by appropriate publication. These parts of the creative process are often neglected by the creative staff, who may harbor the mistaken idea that these necessary steps are somehow outside, even beneath, their competency. Sometimes they feel that, having removed Socrates' thorn from their own minds, they have done their job. Perhaps so, but until their findings are available to others they will have wasted their energies. How can anyone be soothed by an unscored symphony? Inspired by an unpainted picture or a poem that lies hidden in the poet's mind? How can you feed your family with food that you haven't yet brought home? How, indeed, can you expect results from a mental solution to any kind of a problem if you don't do something about it?

Elsewhere we have noted that the report of progress of your creative thinking is useful to you in going farther. Certainly, the mere process of thinking out a report helps you. What have you done? How far have you progressed

toward your goal? Have you learned anything to change
the direction you ought to take? Merely answering such
questions will force you to focus specifically on the matter
in hand and assess what you have done. While careful reports cannot substitute for creative thinking, they can and
do go a long way to place the work in the most favorable
light, important when promotions are considered. Adequate
interim reports are guiding lights to further progress. That
cannot be overemphasized. As Francis Bacon once put it,
"Writing maketh an exact man," and nowhere is exactness so necessary as in this kind of creative thinking.

Many scientific people seem reluctant to make reports,
perhaps because they feel that their mastery of language
is less than adequate. Few instructors impress on students
of science that language is important and valuable as the
fundamental tool of thinking. Without words, thoughts
are mere sensations and impossible to transmit to another
person. With words, one acquires an important ability to
express gradually shaded sensations and a widened range
of relationships that he could not think until he knew
words for them. As one's thinking develops and embraces
the varied concepts of science, special vocabularies are
essential, but the basic values of language are not changed
simply by the addition of more words to the stock one
uses daily.

Students of science must be able to use language, both
spoken and written, as a tool of their calling and with as
much ease as they use a balance, a logarithm table, a
microscope, or a buret. Students spend much time learning
to use each of these specialized tools of the craft, but because language is not characteristic of, nor a monopoly of,
science (it cannot be requisitioned from the storeroom),
they consider it of only secondary interest. If a student
would devote something like the enthusiasm to language
that he does to learning the other tools of his profession,
not only would he himself benefit, but all others would be
aided to a clearer understanding of just what he might add

to knowledge. Original thinking is expressed in new and original relations between two or more concepts, and relations can only be thought of in the terms of language. Exact, or what we commonly call scientific, thinking can only be accomplished by the use of words selected for their exactness and related to one another with equal accuracy.

Some years ago, a very wise man said, "In this scientific age, no one has as much of value to tell the world at large as our scientists; yet no one is less able to tell it." In the past decades, that situation has materially improved through the efforts of the scientific organizations, the companies employing science as an essential part of their businesses, and the heightened awareness and interest of scientists themselves. No longer does science hide away in ivory towers, but rather, it has come out into broader and closer contact with people generally. That places a special burden on every creative thinker, and especially on every scientist: to learn and practice the arts of communication. Both within the relatively narrow sphere of his immediate environment and beyond that to the farthest horizons he can reach, this growing responsibility of the scientist extends. Both by the written report and by word of mouth, every young scientist must be able to explain himself, his work, his objectives, and his findings so that all may understand.

Unfortunately, many young scientists learn new vocabularies to designate the unfamiliar things and ideas encountered in their new pursuit, but forget that grammar and rhetoric are equally as important in making clear the relations between new ideas. It is as if, upon learning something of trigonometry, a student should suddenly decide that arithmetic is no longer of any use to him; or, learning to drive an automobile, that he should forget how to walk.

A satisfying and practical discussion of language as a tool is *The Art of Plain Talk* by Rudolf Flesch, published by Harper & Brothers. This little book will bountifully reward anyone who studies it by giving him a surer command of this vital tool.

Viewed as a tool, language ceases to be a bore and takes on new and exciting aspects of supreme importance to everyone, particularly to scientists.

As we shall see in discussing patents later, the series of reports the investigator makes to himself, or for others, forms an important part of his preparation for applying for a patent. For the moment, let us leave the question of reports and think of the essential step of establishing some reasonable approximation of the value of our creative thinking.

Perhaps no other phase of a research is more important than its evaluation. The usual practice is to guess early that a certain result will be worthwhile and then, when a result is reached and is ready to apply or to sell, to examine the whole thing again in an effort to establish its reasonable value. Actually, the evaluation is best when it is a continuous process. Each time some new phase of the investigation is undertaken, the researcher must estimate in some manner that its probable value will be greater than its probable cost.

Academic research yields its return in satisfaction for the investigator, and requires only that his interest be kept alive by the possibilities that he can envision. Without this continuing interest, that kind of research stops.

In industry, no investigation or development can long proceed unless those responsible see some reasonable probability of an adequate return on accumulating costs. And no problem is more vexing than that of deciding when to abandon a project and write it off to profit and loss. William B. Bell, who was president of American Cyanamid Co., in discussing the executive's view of research, pointed out that one of the greatest needs of executives is a test that will surely indicate whether a particular research should be continued or dropped. He feared to drop an expensive project lest he lose legitimate return or to continue financing a dead issue—to fail to distinguish a potential winner from a dead horse. He wished for an indicator that would show green so long as the probabilities favored continuing a project, but that would turn red as soon as the expectations pointed to loss instead of profit. How convenient! But, lacking that, one must seek to establish value by indirection. That requires, first, an understanding of the nature of such ventures and then an analysis of the specific problem against that background.

The peculiar qualities of research-based enterprises require what the late chemical consultant John E. Teeple called "patient money." Investors who seek the high returns that can be realized through successful ventures of the kind must be fully prepared: (1) to see their investment melt away during the early developmental states of the operation, to watch the tangible assets of their company dwindle and almost, if not quite, disappear; (2) to realize that a substantial part of the investment has been transformed into the intangible assets of experience, "know-how," processes, patents, and like attributes valuable only (or largely) to a going business that has not yet come into being; and (3) to learn that first estimates of capital needed usually fall short of reality and that growing intangible assets are accompanied by troubles equally strange and intangible, not at all the kinds of things that trouble ordinary businesses. Furthermore, the optimistic creators of the venture's intangibles are one day astounded to find that the world has not been waiting for their product, but that the result of their labors has suddenly become a sales problem. Strange, too, is the awakening to the fact that this sales problem is like every other sales problem, only more so.

After a process or product has approval from the laboratory staff, it is not yet an assured success. It then faces the hazards of all new commercial ventures. The question still is: "Does the public want it?" Telling people about a new product can be far more expensive than the research leading up to it. Common experience shows that the cost of impressing upon the public even its name can be ten times that of the experimental and development work that led to its production.

Not all achievements of chemical research are attained by laboratory investigations and many are commercial rather than chemical. Some years ago, Herbert H. Dow founded Dow Chemical Company on a process for recovering bromine, and hence bromides, from Michigan brine. As his business grew, it annoyed the German producers of bromine and bromides who had previously monopolized the American market. Their tactic was to reduce the prices of their products in this market below Dow's probable costs, expecting thereby to force the young company out of business. Meanwhile, they raised their prices in the German market to offset the loss they were taking here. But Dow did not fade away into bankruptcy! Instead, he took his products off of the American market and sold them in Germany, where the German monopolists had raised the price to an excessively high level! Mr. Dow was not only skilled in chemistry and chemical engineering, but he used his active brain in business too.

Investors in research-based enterprises face different problems from those of others. You do not simply walk up to the bank cashier, put down your money, and thereafter draw your interest regularly. Even if the research has come complete from the laboratory, it still must survive the more expensive development stage in the pilot plant and the later, far greater, costs of going into production. Furthermore, each of these money-demanding steps is long, usually several years, and progressively more expensive. The laboratory stage itself is quite indeterminate and may extend over months (in the lucky exceptional case), or over years if no fairy godmother helps the researcher. After the laboratory stage is complete, development may cost several times as much, and the final going into production on a scale that could become profitable costs several times as much as that. Back in the period between the two world wars, people in the chemical industry used to estimate that the average period from complete research to production is about seven years, with the cost running at least ten or a dozen times as great over this seven years as the cost of the laboratory work on which it was based. Later experience during World War II showed that pressure and faster expenditure can often substantially shorten the gap between laboratory and profitable production. But it is far from proved that this effects a real economy. Certainly it does not—and cannot —insure against the constant risk of failure at every step from the original conception of the idea to the final successful production and marketing of the product. No one has yet discovered Mr. Bell's magical indicator that will change color dependably to label either a sure winner or a dead horse—that will show whether more effort is courageous persistence in developing a great idea, or bullheaded stubbornness in clinging to a silly notion.

Perhaps there is no greater disappointment than to have survived all the hazards of giving birth to a great idea, only to have someone else cut the ground out from under your brainchild just when it is beginning to be worthwhile. Here again you need an efficient second sight, a magical extra sense of the future, that will warn you of pitfalls before you reach them. Sometimes, the pit is dug by someone quite outside of your range, the "new competition" we used to call it. That happened to the beautiful scheme for using solid carbon dioxide in household refrigerators that we discussed earlier. Midgley's fluorocarbons came along just in time to revolutionize small refrigerating units at the crucial moment and our solid carbon dioxide system was left at the post—not a dead horse, but one that was stillborn. The only way to avoid that kind of failure is clearly a matter of extrasensory perception.

But our patent system does provide protection in several ways against pirating of your idea by another or against a second finisher who has reached very much the same conclusion you have. To use patents effectively, you must understand just what they are and what privileges a patent gives you. Our laws of patents and copyrights grow out of a provision of the Constitution of the United States:

"The Congress shall have power . . . to promote the progress of science and the useful arts by securing for limited times to authors and inventors the exclusive rights to their respective writings and inventions."

Note that the purpose is "to promote progress" and not necessarily to enrich inventors. The law growing out of this provides broadly that the originator receives the right, not to practice his invention, but to exclude others from doing so for a limited time—seventeen years in the case of a patent, longer for a copyright. Robert E. Wilson, late chairman of the Standard Oil Company (Indiana), expressed it well:

"Our patent system was not created to enrich inventors but to benefit the public by encouraging the invention and the development of new and useful processes and products. . . . Lincoln well summarized the whole situation in his laconic statement that 'the patent system added the fuel of interest to the fire of genius.' "

The intention is clear: to grant the inventor for a limited period the right to exclude others from using what he has invented, this in return for the inventor's full disclosure of his invention. After the term of the patent has run out, the right expires and the invention becomes public property. The value to the public of such disclosure is great enough to justify the temporary monopoly granted the inventor and the term of the patent is presumed to be long enough for the inventor to have profited from his invention. The situation contrasts to the practice of some inventors to keep their inventions secret, a dubious policy at best, but one that could under the most favorable circumstances extend the inventor's monopoly indefinitely. Secrecy is a hazardous policy since it will seldom stand up against a competitor with a first-rate research team bent upon unraveling the method employed in secret to make a particular product. The kind of metallic equipment used can often be revealed by an ultraviolet spectroscope—an instrument so sensitive that it will reveal, as we noted before, the presence of silver in a cup of coffee after a sterling spoon has been dipped in it. Or the infrared spectrometer may let the competitor know much about the secret process by revealing traces of organic raw materials carried over into the finished product as impurities. And then there is always the possibility that a trusted employee may become disgruntled and hire himself out to the competition!

Only two aspects of patents need become the personal concern of the research man: (1) since his employment is primarily concerned with the creation of new things for the benefit of his employer, he will normally be required to enter an agreement with his employer to surrender certain rights to him covering inventions and patents for them, which agreement is affected by patent law; and (2) in carrying out the provisions of such an agreement, the research man must take certain precautions in his daily labors to insure that his employer obtain these benefits as easily and as fully as possible. These two phases the researcher himself should know, but he would be much better advised to leave other aspects to the knowledge and experience of a specialist in patent law rather than to depend upon his own scant knowledge.

The employment contract often confronts the prospective researcher with its odd stipulations and this unexpected strange subject may suggest that something is about to be put over on him. The procedure is quite orthodox. The employer seeks to avoid possible future misunderstandings by agreeing with his employee on certain crucial points in advance of trouble. By expressing these conditions of employment in a contract, both parties can avoid trouble through inadvertence.

A few basic principles govern employment contracts. Fundamentally, the employee agrees in such a contract: (1) to do certain types of work for his employer and for his employer's benefit; (2) to preserve the employer's confidence in all matters affecting the business; (3) to make and to assign to his employer any patent applications arising out of his employment; and (4) to avoid giving the employer's competitors the benefit of his specialized knowledge and experience gained in the employer's activities. These are, of course, reasonable conditions any employer would expect to govern.

On his side, the employer agrees: (1) to pay the employee wages at stated intervals and in specified amounts; (2) to provide facilities for the employee's use in doing his work; and (3) otherwise to provide for the employee's welfare during, and for some specified period after, his employment.

Those broad principles contain no cause for misunderstanding or unpleasantness, so long as they are understood in advance. Only when either party attempts to go beyond such reasonable provisions and to make a contract extend to minute details of conduct is trouble likely to arise.

Obviously, the simpler a contract can be made the better. There is no inducement on either side to break a contract which is reasonable and which represents an exchange of values satisfactory to both parties. The fewer conditions a contract seeks to impose, the less likely it is to become onerous.

The provision of the contract that the employee assist in every way to secure for the employer the exclusive benefit of the employee's inventions places an important responsibility on the employee. He must be prepared at any future time to testify, in court if necessary, to the exact times and circumstances that certain experiments were performed, certain ideas conceived, and certain actions taken.

This requires records, for no active human mind can maintain a continuous memory of all the events of a busy life over a long stretch of years. Furthermore, the records most effective in refreshing the memory and possessing the greatest weight in a subsequent inquiry are written out in longhand at the time by the person whose memory is being refreshed, and take the form of a continuing diary in a bound book. Unrecorded thoughts might as well never have existed.

Several reasons for the importance of these characteristics of the written record appear on close examination. Most important is the fact that the record itself can call to the mind of the person who wrote it many other circumstances extending and amplifying the written words by associations of ideas. A good record for patent purposes must be more or less continuous over a period of time and set down chronologically. A diary, in other words. Records made in one's own handwriting are more valuable than others primarily because alterations of any kind by someone else are usually obvious.

Finally, the record should be kept in a permanently bound book. Entries made in order on the pages are more difficult to lose or to disarrange than are loose sheets, and a bound book by its very nature encourages orderly records.

This has been set down without reference to other considerations involved in patents and their relative weights. The researcher need not burden himself with such ideas, but rather, entrust them to someone else better equipped to evaluate a man's work than he himself and better able to take the several steps toward an issued patent.

Having thus traced our part in the creative process from the germ of the idea to its final patentable form, it remains only to bring together loose ends of this discussion and to add suggestions of places where the reader can learn more details. That we shall do in the next chapter.

CHAPTER 11

Some Thoughts from Great Minds

If this discussion has seemed to emphasize research in chemical industry, sometimes to the exclusion of other fields of creativity, it has done so for the very good reason that that has been the author's environment over a number of decades. The principles employed in chemical research are equally valid in the most diverse areas. The creative process that yields a method of mining magnesium or bromine from the ocean differs only in the subject matter on which it operates from that which produces a symphony, a poem, a painting. The "thorn in the mind" is different for each and the medium used is suited to the particular purpose, but, whatever the stimulus and the medium of the final expression, the process of assembling ideas, impressions, sensations into a final synthesis is basically the same. We have chosen to designate the process as it is applied to scientific materials and ideas as the "scientific method"; but it is only right to acknowledge here that not everyone agrees that there is a special and separate scientific method. No less eminent an authority than Dr. James Bryant Conant, former president of Harvard University and an eminent key person in the atomic energy program of World War II, as well as in education generally, views the broad sweep of creative endeavor and dubs it the *alleged* scientific method. A few years ago, the Institute of Industrial Research, an organization of leading directors of industrial research, devoted one of its national meetings to the subject of creativity and listened not to other industrial research directors, but to a philosopher, an economist, a businessman, a painter, a composer, and a poet. Whether you call it the scientific method, as I have, or leave it as merely creative thinking, the fact remains that the fruitfulness of our thinking can be materially improved if we follow methods others have proved successful in the past, whatever may have been their medium.

Perhaps this theme can be best illustrated by quoting from eminently creative persons in a variety of fields as we do now:

Creative genius is the ability to effect unusual combinations of elements nobody else would think of putting together, and to do so in a way that makes the combination click. That goes for genius in any form: artistic, literary or musical; inventive or scientific; military, political or economic.

The born genius does this instinctively, in a flash—often an emotional one.

But there are deliberate geniuses, who achieve as striking results in cold blood. They reach out, literally or figuratively, for totally unrelated elements, consider how they may be combined, effect the combination, adjust it until it works—and behold! They have a something altogether new.

Most commonly this process is directed toward a clearly defined end—as in the case of Edison's search for a filament to make practicable the incandescent lamp. This is the pattern for a great deal of present-day industrial development research. It is the pattern for much creative work in the design of intangible things—sales plans, for example.

But the procedure can be applied sometimes even more successfully to producing a startling effect for which a use will be found afterward. This is sometimes done in businesses of which originality is the true lifeblood—advertising, for example. By deliberate synthesis of wildly incongruous elements, "picked out of the air" at random, a lot of ideas are evolved, some good, some bad, some indifferent—and one, perhaps, terrific. Try this on a puzzling situation, adapting it to fit, and you have what the outsider would consider a flash of inspiration. Actually, it is brilliant, but by deliberate contrivance, not inspiration.

—*Robert R. Updegraff* (publicist)—"Shake Well—and See What Happens" in *Management Briefs* (No. 77)

Science is built up of successive solutions given to questions of ever increasing subtlety approaching nearer and nearer towards the very essence of phenomena.

—*Justus von Liebig* (eminent German chemist)

Contrary to popular belief, creative thinking is not a native "gift" but, rather, a discipline that may be developed through practice.

—*Dorothy W. Parr* (author, editor)

An erroneous impression, fostered by sensational popular biography, is that scientific discovery is often made by inspiration—a sort of coup de foudre—from on high. This is rarely the case. Even Archimedes' sudden inspiration in the bathtub; Newton's experience in the apple orchard; Descartes' geometrical discoveries in his bed; Darwin's flash of lucidity on reading a passage in Malthus; Kekule's vision of the closed carbon ring which came to him on top of a London bus; and Einstein's brilliant solution of the Michelson puzzle in the patent office in Berne, were not messages out of the blue. They were the final co-ordinations by minds of genius of innumerable accumulated facts and impressions which lesser men could grasp only in their uncorrelated isolation, but which—by them—were seen in entirety and integrated into general principles. The scientist takes off from the manifold observations of predecessors, and shows his intelligence, if any, by his ability to discriminate between the important and the negligible, by selecting here and there the significant stepping-stones that will lead across the difficulties to new understanding. The one who places the last stone and steps across to the terra firma of accomplished discovery gets all the credit. Only the initiated know and honor those whose patient integrity and devotion to exact observation have made the last step possible.

—*Hans Zinsser* (bacteriologist) "As I Remember Him,"
Atlantic Monthly Press and Little, Brown & Co.

Tyndall emphasized the extreme value of the two little words "as if" when used by the scientific mind, showing how, from things seen, a scientific imagination can lay bare things unseen and make possible discoveries of great value. Discoveries often come by accident, but the imaginative mind sees in these discoveries future possibilities. The imaginative mind, following out discoveries so made, is led into unlimited fields of usefulness. We must not think, however, of imagination as being the sole factor, although it is probably the principal factor, in the production of valuable materials. There must be energy, concentration, and persistence, which will carry such a mind across the Jordan into the promised land. Nevertheless, the imagination is the most important factor here, because, without it, there would be no promised land.

 —*Gustave W. Thompson* (research director)—*Ind. Eng.*
Chem. 6, 1958 (1914)

My industry has been nearly as great as it could have been in the observation and collection of facts. What is far more important, my love of natural science has been steady and ardent.

By collecting all the facts which bore in any way on the variation of animals and plants under domestication and nature, some light might perhaps be thrown on the whole subject. My first notebook was opened in July 1837. I worked on true Baconian principles, and, without any theory, collected facts on a wholesale scale, more especially with respect to domesticated productions, by printed inquiries, by conversation with skilfull breeders and gardeners, and by extensive reading. When I see the list of books of all kinds which I read and abstracted, including whole series of Journals and Transactions, I am surprised at my industry. I soon perceived that selection was the keystone of man's success in making useful races of animals and plants. But how selection could be applied to organisms living in a state of nature remained for some time a mystery to me.

In October 1838—that is, fifteen months after I had begun my systematic enquiry—I happened to read for amusement Malthus on population, and being well prepared to appreciate the struggle for existence which everywhere goes on from long-continued observation of the habits of animals and plants, it at once struck me that under these circumstances favourable variations would tend to be preserved, and unfavourable ones to be destroyed. The result of this would be the formation of new species.

Here, then, I had at last got a theory by which to work; but I was so anxious to avoid prejudice that I determined not for some time to write even the briefest sketch of it. In June 1842, I first allowed myself the satisfaction of writing a very brief abstract of my theory in pencil in 35 pages; and this was enlarged during the summer of 1844 into one of 230 pages, which I had fairly copied out and still possess.

But at that time I overlooked one problem of great importance; and it is astonishing to me, except on the principle of Columbus and his egg, that I could have overlooked it and its solution. This problem is the tendency in organic beings descended from the same stock to diverge greatly in character as they become modified. That they have diverged greatly is obvious from the manner in which species of all kinds can be classed under genera, genera under families, families under sub-orders, and so forth; and I can remember the very spot in the road, whilst in my carriage, when to my joy the solution occurred to me; and this was long after I had come to Down. The solution, as I believe, is that the modified offspring of all dominant and increasing forms tend to become adapted to many and highly diversified places in the economy of nature.

—Charles Darwin

Establish the facts by direct, frequent, and careful observations, and check them repeatedly one against the other; these facts will be your premises. When many variables are related, find out what happens when only one is allowed to vary, the others remaining constant. Multiply such experiments as much as you can, and make them with the utmost precision in your power. Draw your conclusions and express them in mathematical language if possible. Apply all your mathematical resources to the transformation of the equations; confront the new equations thus obtained with reality. That is, see what they mean, which group of facts they represent. Make new experiments on the basis of these new facts, etc. And repeat the process as often as may be necessary.

—George Sarton (historian of science)*—History of Science,*
Harvard University Press

The leaders of industries frequently need improvements in their processes, and even new discoveries or inventions which will extend their activities. It is thus logical, and often extremely profitable, to organize research laboratories to solve specific problems. Efficiency requires that the director shall assign to each worker a carefully planned program. Experiments which do not logically fit in with this program are to be discouraged. This type of industrial research has frequently been very successful in solving specific problems, but usually along lines already foreseen.

This method, however, has serious limitations. Directors are rare who can foresee the solutions sufficiently well to plan out a good campaign of attack in advance. Then, too, the best type of research man does not like to be told too definitely what must be the objects of his experiments. To him scientific curiosity is usually a greater incentive than the hope of commercially useful results. Fortunately, however, with proper encouragement, this curiosity itself is a guide that may lead to fundamental discoveries, and thus may solve the specific problems in still better ways than could have been reached by a direct attack; or may lead to valuable by-products.

—Irving Langmuir (chemist)*—Ind. Eng. Chem. 20,* 335
(1928)

All these (early flying) machines may be not inappropriately classified as devices of engineers to achieve flight by invention—call it practical experiment if you will—before the principles of dynamic motion had been studied. The practical man makes his machine first and lets experience decide whether its design is sound or not; the scientific man begins by investigating the principles involved in the problem, and then suggests how they may be met. The only satisfactory way to determine such principles is by experiment and calculations based upon the results.

—Sir Richard Gregory (English scientist)*—Discovery,*
The Macmillan Company

Necessity is not the mother of invention; knowledge and experiment are its parents. This is clearly seen to be the case of many industrial discoveries; high-speed cutting tools were not a necessity which preceded, but an application which followed, the discovery of the properties of tungsten-chromium-iron alloys; so, too, the use of titanium arc lamps and vanadium in steel were sequels to the industrial preparation of these metals, and not discoveries made by sheer force of necessity.

—*W. R. Whitney* (research director)—in *Discovery* by
Sir Richard Gregory

The most apparent and probably the most impressive differences between research today and forty years ago are the prodigious scale on which it is now conducted and the incredible diversity of activities to which the scientific method is applied. . . . We no longer await the explosions of inventive genius. Our present system of organized research places in the hands of genius all the facilities at our command, thus not only hastening his progress but providing the best means of translating his results promptly to utilitarian purposes. The system has further advantages. The cumulative results of the day-to-day application of scientific methods in our research laboratories has given mankind many of the beneficent things we did not have twenty, ten, or even five years ago.

—*Frederick M. Becket* (electrometallurgist)—*Trans. Amer.*
Electrochem. Soc., 72, 14 (1937)

What is likely to stand out about 20th century America when history balances accounts? Hubert Heffner, of Stanford University, singles out the organized pursuit of scientific research as our most important imprint on world civilization. . . . There are some genuine problems, however, and foremost is our failure so far to define clearly basic research goals. Defense and conquest of disease are frequently cited justifications for public support [of research in our universities by government]. But more important is the benefit accruing to education itself and the quality of American life. . . . New knowledge leads to new products, new jobs, and—if wisely employed—increased well-being.

—Editorial in the *Clearwater Sun*

There seems to be a striking similarity between the processes used in scientific inquiry and the processes man makes use of in building up the assumptive world. Both science and common sense can be regarded as functional activities man uses in carrying out his life transactions. And the method of scientific inquiry seems in many ways to be an unconscious imitation of those age-old processes man has employed in his common-sense solutions of problems. In common-sense activity, the assumptions and awarenesses on which man depends for effective action are the hypotheses he has built up from his many experiences; weighted averages he unconsciously uses to give him a high prognosis for effective action.

There are, however, certain important differences between the steps involved in pursuing scientific inquiry and the apparent processes that constitute common sense. A most important difference is the fact that in using scientific inquiry, man is the operator who decides what he is going to operate on and how. In an everyday life situation, however, man is not only the operator but he is also being operated on and must carry out his activities in the midst of the situation itself. When we meet hitches in everyday life and try to overcome them with hunches for effective action, we test these hunches by the action itself in a more or less insightful, more or less conscious way. In scientific inquiry, on the other hand, hunches are tested by controlled experiments and a deliberate attempt is made to intellectualize the processes involved.

—Cantril, Ames, Hastorf, and Ittleson—"Psychology and Scientific Research" in *Science* (Nov. 4, 1949)

The historians of the future may well select the development of deliberate creativeness as the most important development in this century. We have passed through the age of random creativeness and are entering an age of deliberate creativeness. With this technique there is almost certainty that we can fulfill our needs, desires and whims in the future. The rate at which we can develop will be increased enormously and, if the same or analogous techniques are applied to other fields, man will not only be mindful of himself, but will understand himself and his interactions with his environments. What we have today is wonderful; but what there will be tomorrow will be much better.

—*Maurice Nelles* (research chemist) in *The Chemical Bulletin*, ACS

A great part of every man's life must be employed in collecting materials for the exercise of genius. Invention, strictly speaking, is little more than a new combination of those images which have been previously gathered and deposited in the memory; nothing can come of nothing; he who has laid up no material can produce no combinations. The more extensive, therefore, your acquaintance is with the works of those who have excelled, the more extensive will be your powers of invention, and what may appear still more like a paradox, the more original will be your conceptions.

—*Sir Joshua Reynolds* (English painter)

Mathematical creation does not consist in making new combinations with mathematical entities already known. Anyone could do that, but the combinations so made would be infinite in number and most of them absolutely without interest. To create consists precisely in not making useless combinations and in making those which are useful and which are only a small minority. Invention is discernment, choice . . . Mathematical creation is not simply mechanical—it could not be done by a machine however perfect. It is not merely a question of applying rules, of making the most combinations possible according to certain fixed laws. The combinations so obtained would be exceedingly numerous, useless and cumbersome. The true work of the inventor consists in choosing among these combinations so as to eliminate the useless ones, or rather to avoid the trouble of making them.

—*Henri Poincaré* (French mathematician)—*Science and Hypothesis*, Dover Publications (1952)

This worthless present [*The Rival-Ladies*] was designed for you long before it was a play; when it was only a confused mass of thoughts, tumbling over one another in the dark; when the fancy was yet in its first work, moving the sleeping images of things towards the light, there to be distinguished, and then chosen or rejected by the judgment; it was yours, my lord, before I could call it mine. . . . In that first tumult of my thoughts, there appeared a disorderly kind of beauty in some of them, which gave me hope something . . . might be drawn from them.

—*John Dryden* (English poet)

I do not believe that inspiration falls from heaven. I think it rather the result of a profound indolence and of our incapacity to put to work certain forces within ourselves. These unknown forces work deep within us, with the aid of the elements of daily life, its scenes and passions. When they burden us and oblige us to conquer the kind of somnolence in which we indulge ourselves like invalids who try to prolong the dream and dread resuming contact with reality, in short when the work that makes itself in us and in spite of us demands to be born, we can believe that this work comes to us from beyond and is offered to us by the gods . . . The play I am producing is a visitation of this sort. I was sick and tired of writing, when one morning, after having slept poorly, I woke with a start and witnessed, as from a seat in a theatre, three acts which brought to life an epoch and characters about which I had no documentary information and which I regarded moreover as forbidding. Long afterward I succeeded in writing the play and I divined the circumstances that must have served to incite me.

—*Jean Cocteau*—(French playwright) "Le Foyer des Artistes," Libraire Plon, Les Petits-Fils de Plon et Nourrit, Paris

The fact is that disorder is the condition of the mind's fertility: it contains the mind's promise, since its fertility depends on the unexpected rather than the expected, depends rather on what we do not know, and because we do not know it, than what we know. How could it be otherwise? The domain I am trying to survey is limitless, but the whole is reduced to human proportions at once if we take care to stick to our own experience, to the observations we have ourselves made, to the means we have tested.

    —*Paul Valéry* (French poet)—"A Course in Poetics: First Lesson" in *Southern Review, 5,* No. 3, Louisiana State University Press (1940)

The general progress of the three books which I was to write in the next four and a half years could be fairly described in this way. It was a progress that began in a whirling vortex and a creative chaos and that proceeded slowly at the expense of infinite confusion, toil and error toward clarification and the articulation of an ordered and formal structure. An extraordinary image remains with me from that year, the year I spent abroad when the material of these books first began to take on articulate form. It seemed that I had inside me, swelling and gathering all the time, a huge black cloud, and that this was loaded with electricity, pregnant, crested, with a kind of hurricane violence that could not be held in check much longer; that the moment was approaching fast when it must break. Well, all I can say is that the storm did break. It broke that summer in Switzerland. It came in torrents, and it is not over yet.

I cannot really say the book was written. It was something that took hold of me and possessed me, and before I was done with it—that is, before I finally emerged with the first completed part—it seemed to me that it had done for me. It was exactly as if this great black storm cloud had opened up and, mid flashes of lightning, was pouring from its depth a torrential and ungovernable flood. Upon that flood everything was swept and borne along as by a great river. And I was borne along with it.

    —*Thomas Wolfe* (American novelist)—*Story of a Novel,* Scribners, 1936

A final word on creative imagination. Besides the intellectual factors, certain emotional ones are demanded. The unconscious work goes on only over problems that are important to the waking mind, only when the mind's possessor worries about them, only when he cares, passionately.

    —*R. W. Gerard* (American physiologist in *The Scientific Monthly,* June 1946

No amount of experimentation can ever prove me right; a single experiment may at any time prove me wrong.
     —*Albert Einstein* (theoretical physicist) in *The Practical Cogitator,* Houghton Mifflin

That is the great tragedy of science—the slaying of a beautiful hypothesis by a single ugly fact.
     —*Thomas Huxley* (English physiologist)

A theory is good only as long as it is useful.
     —*Henri Poincaré*

The method which our race has found most effective in acquiring knowledge is by this time familiar to all men. It is the method of modern science—that process which consists in an interrogation of Nature entirely dispassionate, patient, systematic; such careful experiment and cumulative record as can often elicit from her slightest indications her deepest truths. That method is now dominant throughout the civilized world; and although in many directions experiments may be difficult and dubious, facts rare and elusive, science works slowly on and bides her time—refusing to fall back upon tradition or to launch into speculation merely because strait is the gate which leads to valid discovery, indisputable truth.
     —*F. W. H. Myers* (English essayist and poet) in *Discovery* by Sir Richard Gregory

The formulation of a problem is often more essential than its solution, which may be merely a matter of mathematical or experimental skill.
     Physical concepts are free creations of the human mind, and are not, however it may seem, uniquely determined by the external world.

     —*Albert Einstein*

What is then the quality which enables some men to achieve great things in scientific research? For greatest achievements men must have genius—that elusive quality that so often passes unrecognized, while high ability receives reward and praise. But for achievements genius is not enough, and for all but the greatest achievements, not necessary. What does appear essential for real achievement in scientific research is a combination of qualities, by no means frequent, but commoner than is genius. It seems that these qualities are clarity of mind, a combination of imagination and caution, of receptivity and scepticism, of patience and thoroughness and of ability to finalize, of intellectual honesty, of a love of discovery of new knowledge and understanding, and of singleness of purpose. Of these the most important is the love of discovery of new knowledge and understanding. If any young readers, contemplating scientific research as a profession, do not feel this love . . . scientific research is not for them.

—Paul Freedman—*The Principles of Scientific Research,*
Public Affairs Press, Washington (1950)

Undoubtedly no amount of training will develop any fruitful imagination in those devoid of that gift. But in those who have a natural gift of imagination, training can either stifle it or help it to develop into a controlled, scientific imagination, which is very different from the unrestricted imagination of the unscientific mind.

—*Paul Freedman*

To draw the parallel strands of scientific knowledge into a firm fabric of industrial accomplishment a man must know how to gear his work to satisfying the specific needs of present or potential customers. A new product is not good because it is hard or durable; it can only be good because it satisfies the specific needs of some particular type of use or some particular customer. Therefore, this work must be carried out not only with a knowledge of scientific principles, but also with an active interest in and knowledge of practical field situations. . . . Over the years industrial research men have come to use broad generalizations and general principles to plan and carry out the programs necessary to solve practical industrial problems with the minimum expenditure of time and money. . . . A new science this is of applying basic scientific principles to the solution of practical problems. One might almost say that we have in a rough manner been developing a new scientific discipline with its own techniques, its own essential

factual background, and its own specific manner of thinking.
     —*Clifford F. Rassweiler* (past president of the American
                                        Chemical Society)

Research is the one function of business which, far more
than any other, deals with the future. . . . Only one reliable
method of forecasting the future has ever been developed, and
that method consists in projecting the continuing trends of
the past.
     —*Roland P. Soule* (chemical engineer, banker) in *Chemical
                    & Metallurgical Engineering,* July 1946

Chapter 12

Some Helpful Books

If this little book has accomplished even part of its purpose, the reader will wish to pursue further the subjects we have considered here. These sources of more elaborate treatments of the creative process have interested and, to a varying extent, inspired me. Perhaps you too will find some or all of them interesting and valuable.

American Management Association. *Getting the Most out of Research and Engineering.* Published by the association, New York, 1954.

Bancroft, Wilder D. *The Methods of Research.* Rice Institute Pamphlet, Volume XV, No. 4, October 1928. Published by the institute, Houston, Texas.

Becket, Frederick M. *Transactions of the American Electrochemical Society, 72,* 14 (1937).

Bergson, Henri. *The Creative Mind.* Translated by Mabelle L. Andison. Philosophical Library, New York, 1951.

Beveridge, W. L. B. *The Art of Scientific Investigation.* W. W. Norton, Co., New York, 1951.

Bush, George P. *Bibliography on Research Administration.* University Press of Washington, D.C., 1954.

Cantril, et al. *Science.* Published by the American Association for the Advancement of Science, November 4, 1949.

Cocteau, Jean. *Le Foyer des Artistes,* Libraire Plon, Les Petits-Fils de Plon et Nourrit, Paris.

Crawford, Robert P. *The Techniques of Creative Thinking.* Hawthorn Books, Inc., New York, 1954.

Fieser, Louis F. *The Scientific Method.* Reinhold Publishing Corp., New York, 1964.

Flesch, Rudolf. *The Art of Clear Thinking.* Harper & Brothers, New York, 1951.

Freedman, Paul. *The Principles of Scientific Research.* Public Affairs Press, Washington, D.C., 1950.

Furnas, C. C. *Research in Industry*. D. VanNostrand Co., Princeton, New Jersey, 1948.

Gerard, R. W. *The Scientific Monthly*, June 1946.

Gregory, Sir Richard. *Discovery*, The Macmillan Company.

Hadamard, Jacques. *The Psychology of Invention in the Mathematical Field*. Dover Publications (reprint), New York, 1954.

Industrial Research Institute. *The Nature of Creative Thinking*. Published by the institute, New York, 1952.

Industrial Research Institute. *Research is People*. New York University Press, 1956.

Kelly, Maurice J. "An Outline of Creative Thinking." *The Chemist*, February 1956, p. 55.

Killeffer, D. H. *The Genius of Industrial Research*. Reinhold Publishing Corp., New York, 1948.

Langmuir, Irving. *Industrial and Engineering Chemistry 20*, 335 (1928).

Lowes, John Livingston. *The Road to Xanadu*. Houghton Mifflin Co., Boston, Massachusetts, 1927.

Moroney, M. J. *Facts from Figures*. Penguin Books, Baltimore, Maryland, 1962.

Morse, Phillip M., and Kimball, George E. *Methods of Operations Research*. The Technology Press, Cambridge, Massachusetts and John Wiley & Sons, Inc., New York, 1950.

Mueller, Robert E. *Inventivity*. John Day Company, New York, 1963.

Osborn, Alex F. *How to Become More Creative*. Charles Scribner's Sons, New York, 1964.

Platt, Washington, and Baker, Ross A. "The Scientific Hunch." *Journal of Chemical Education*, Volume VIII, 1931, p. 1969.

Poincaré, Henri. *Science and Hypothesis*. Translated by Francis Maitland. Dover Publications (reprint), New York, 1952.

Rogers, Carl R. "Toward a Theory of Creativity." *ETC*, Volume XI, No. 4, Summer 1954, p. 249. International Society for General Semantics, Chicago.

Sarton, George. *History of Science*, Harvard University Press, 1959.

Singh, Jagjit. *Great Ideas of Operations Research.* Dover Publications, New York, 1968.

Smyth, Henry D. *Atomic Energy for Military Purposes.* Princeton University Press, Princeton, New Jersey.

Soule, Roland P. *Chemical & Metallurgical Engineering,* July 1946.

Taylor, Jack W. *How to Create Ideas.* Prentice-Hall, New York, 1961.

Thompson, Gustave W. *Industrial and Engineering Chemistry 6,* 158 (1914).

Tumin, Melvin. "Obstacles to Creativity." *ETC,* Volume XI, No. 4, Summer 1954, p. 261. International Society for General Semantics, Chicago.

Wiegand, W. B. "Determinants in Research." *Rubber World,* Volume 142, No. 6, September 1960, p. 71. (Also separate as *Columbian Colloidal Carbons,* Vol. XVIII, No. 1.)

Young, James W. *A Technique of Producing Ideas.* Advertising Publications, Inc., Chicago, 1944.

Index